# Woodwork Design and Practice

## Also by David M. Shaw

Principles and Practice of Woodwork for GCE
Students (with J. M. Reeve)
Design Education for the Middle Years

# Woodwork Design and Practice

## David M. Shaw

David Shaw is an educational adviser for schools to the
Coventry LEA. He was formerly Senior Lecturer in
the Education Unit of Coventry (Lanchester)
Polytechnic. He is a chief examiner for GCE Design
(Advanced) and a visiting examiner for CDT
teacher-training. For some years he was a chief
examiner and moderator/assessor for the CSE.

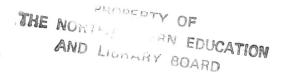
HODDER AND STOUGHTON
LONDON SYDNEY AUCKLAND TORONTO

ISBN  0  340  08206  2

First printed 1973.   Reprinted 1976, 1978, 1979, 1980, 1981, 1983

Filmset by BAS Printers Limited, Wallop,
Hampshire
Printed and bound in Hong Kong
for Hodder and Stoughton Educational,
a division of Hodder and Stoughton Ltd,
Mill Road, Dunton Green, Sevenoaks, Kent
by Colorcraft Ltd.

# Contents

# Author's note

This book is designed to be used by students throughout the whole of the five year Secondary School course and by adults who seek a thorough grounding in the craft of woodworking. For this reason the chapters are arranged so that students will, by and large, progress from the simpler practical techniques, learnt and practised during the earlier stages of study, to the sections on timber technology, design, and projects which are appropriate for the more experienced student.

It is hoped that *Woodwork Design and Practice* will be used both in practical sessions and during study periods, as a source of basic core material, and for revision purposes, and that the final section in particular will serve as a detailed guide to a number of classified woodworking topics.

When this book went to press, some details of the metrication of woodworking tools and hardware were still under active consideration by manufacturers, trade associations, and the British Standards Institution. Certain tool dimensions have therefore been converted to rounded rather than exact metric equivalents of existing equipment sized in Imperial units. This is felt to be justified both because it is unlikely that such tool sizes will be materially altered and because students must learn to think in round metric terms rather than in those which are exact Imperial equivalents.

David M. Shaw

# Acknowledgments

The author wishes to acknowledge the considerable assistance he has received in the preparation of this book, particularly from Mr H. Bestley for his advice on textual material, from Mr B. Chapman for his work in preparing the illustrations for publication, and from the publishers for their help in all pertinent matters. The guidance of the Timber Trade Federation and a number of manufacturers of tools and hardware with regard to metrication in the woodworking industry is also gratefully acknowledged.

Thanks are due to the following for kindly supplying photographs and for granting permission for their reproduction in this book: Fig. 195f, Mr C. G. Benham; Fig. 373c, Mr P. W. Blandford; Fig. 375d, The National Federation of Young Farmers' Clubs (photographer Joan Beard); Fig. 392a, Mr R. Roberts; Fig. 340c, Burgess Products Co Ltd, Electric Tool Division; Figs. 344b and 346e, Stanley-Bridges Ltd; Fig. 351b, Black and Decker Ltd; Figs. 195g, 197 and 201h are of carvings by pupils from Coventry schools.

# 1 Basic Woodworking Techniques

## SAFETY PRECAUTIONS IN THE WORKSHOP

Sharp-edged woodworking tools used with skill and care will produce good work, but careless handling or storage may damage both tools and work, and even injure the user.

Safety first rules for workshop conduct are simple, are based on common sense, and MUST be obeyed!

### Dress

DO roll up your sleeves and tuck in your tie. At the bench a flapping shirt sleeve or dangling tie is always a nuisance, but when using the lathe or other machinery these can cause a serious accident.

Long hair hanging over the face is not just sloppy – it is dangerous!

An apron tied at the back will protect clothes from dust, dirt and oil stains (Fig. 1), but the neck strap should not be too strong – it should snap easily if the apron gets caught in a machine.

### Moving about the workshop

NEVER RUN ABOUT in the workshop. Too much haste when carrying tools may result in a slip, and injury to yourself or someone else. You may knock into another boy at work, causing damage to his job.

ALWAYS carry sharp-edged tools, such as chisels, point downwards.

### Using tools

Use tools only in the way your teacher demonstrates to you. NEVER hold wood with one hand while working on it with a chisel or any edge tool held in the other hand. Should you do so, you will probably cut yourself – almost certainly you will spoil your work. Keep both hands behind the cutting edge of a chisel. Cramp the wood either in a vice or on a bench hook, or cramp it to the top of the bench with a G-cramp or holdfast.

Which will you be?

Sloppy and sorry          Sensible and safe

or

Fig. 1

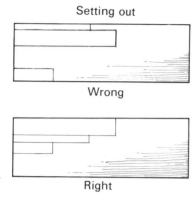

Setting out

Wrong

Right

Fig. 2

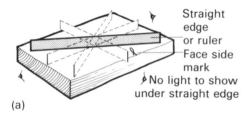

Straight edge or ruler

Face side mark

No light to show under straight edge

(a)

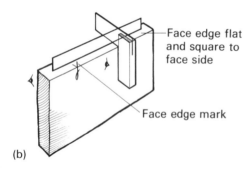

Face edge flat and square to face side

Face edge mark

(b)

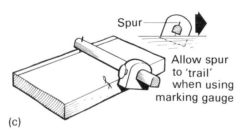

Spur

Allow spur to 'trail' when using marking gauge

(c)

Fig. 3

When putting tools down on the bench, place them in the 'well', away from the bench edge. This is important for two reasons.

(a) Metal tools are likely to break if dropped or knocked on to the floor (e.g. the end of a chisel blade may become chipped, or a cast-iron plane stock broken).

(b) If a chisel or saw blade projects over the edge of the bench, you (or someone else) may be cut by it.

NOTE: *be sure that plane blades and handles are properly secured to their planes – a falling plane blade can cut through the top of a shoe. Hammer and mallet heads must also be firmly wedged on to their handles (see Chapter 9)*

**Storing tools**

Do keep your bench top tidy. Heaps of tools on the bench are:

(a) a nuisance when you are working;

(b) easily damaged;

(c) likely to cause injury to the worker.

When you have finished using the tools – PUT THEM AWAY. That is what a storage rack or tool cupboard is for.

**Machinery and portable powered tools**

NEVER touch any machine unless instructed to do so by your teacher. Before starting it up make sure:

(a) you know exactly how to use it;

(b) you know how to stop it and just where the switch is. (If the machine is new to you, practise starting and stopping it a few times before you actually use it.)

Detailed safety precautions to be taken when using fixed and portable powered tools are given in Chapter 10.

# BASIC PRACTICAL WORK

## Setting out

A cutting list (see page 22) will supply the dimensions of the timber required, including an allowance for sawing and planing – length 15 mm, width 7 mm to 9 mm, and thickness 4 mm to 5 mm. These sizes should be marked out in pencil on the board. Be careful to cut so as to avoid wasting timber (Fig. 2).

## Cutting and planing to size

After sawing the wood along the pencil marks, using rip and cross cut saws (see Chapter 9), use a jack plane to prepare each piece to size.

Step 1 Select, plane and test the FACE SIDE, putting on the FACE SIDE MARK only when the wood is quite flat (Fig. 3a).

Step 2 Plane and test FACE EDGE, and put on FACE EDGE MARK when true (Fig. 3b).

Step 3 Gauge to WIDTH (Fig. 3c), plane to the gauge mark and check as in Fig. 3b.

Step 4 Gauge to THICKNESS (Fig. 3d), plane to the gauge mark and check as in Fig. 3a.

Step 5 Using marking knife, try square and rule, SQUARE ENDS to the correct length, and saw to the waste side of the lines using a tenon saw (Fig. 3e and f).

Step 6 If required, plane end grain with a finely set smoothing plane, using one of the methods shown in Fig. 3g to i, and test as in Fig. 3j.

Fig. 3

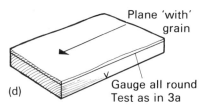

(d) Plane 'with' grain
Gauge all round
Test as in 3a

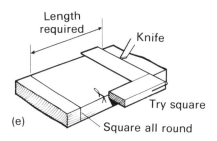

(e) Length required
Knife
Try square
Square all round

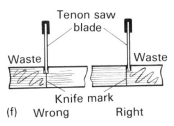

Tenon saw blade
Waste    Waste
Knife mark
(f)    Wrong    Right

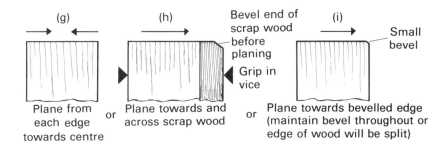

(g) Plane from each edge towards centre

or

(h) Plane towards and across scrap wood

Bevel end of scrap wood before planing
Grip in vice

or

(i) Small bevel
Plane towards bevelled edge (maintain bevel throughout or edge of wood will be split)

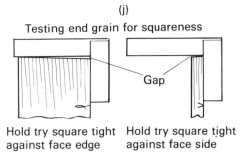

(j) Testing end grain for squareness
Gap
Hold try square tight against face edge    Hold try square tight against face side

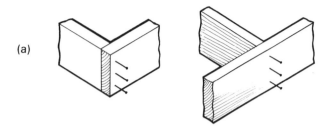

(a)

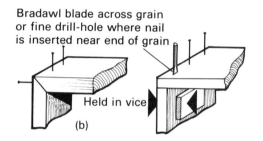

Bradawl blade across grain or fine drill-hole where nail is inserted near end of grain

Held in vice

(b)

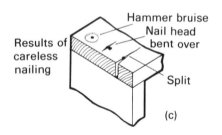

Results of careless nailing

Hammer bruise
Nail head
bent over

Split

(c)

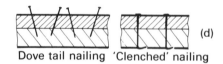

Dove tail nailing    'Clenched' nailing

(d)

Fig. 4

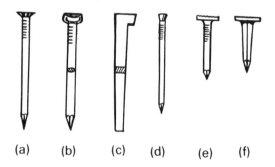

(a)    (b)    (c)    (d)    (e)    (f)

Fig. 5

## JOINTING WOOD

### Nailing

The simplest way of jointing wood is to nail it together (Fig. 4a), but to do this without splitting the wood and yet make a strong job requires care (Fig. 4b and c). Fig. 4d shows how nails may be arranged to help prevent their being pulled out or working loose. Different types of nail have their own special uses (Fig. 5a to f).

### Round wire nail (French nail)

12 mm to 150 mm (Fig. 5a). This nail has a round flat head and round shank. The head is roughened to prevent the hammer face from slipping off it and the 'neck' or the shank is roughened to give a better grip in the wood. Used for making packing cases, boxes, and for rough carpentry.

### Oval wire nail

12 mm to 150 mm (Fig. 5b). The oval section of this nail is less likely to split the wood than a round wire nail if used as shown in Fig. 5g. It also gives a better grip on the wood than the French nail. Its small head can be punched below the surface of the wood and 'stopped'.

### Cut nail

25 mm to 200 mm (Fig. 5c). This nail is cut or stamped from mild steel sheet and is used for heavy constructional work. It gives a better grip on the wood than a wire nail.

### Panel Pin

10 mm to 50 mm (Fig. 5d). The panel pin is made in different gauges (diameters) from mild steel or brass wire. Like the oval wire nail, its head may be punched below the surface of the wood. It is used for fixing mouldings and other similar light work.

### Roofing clout

15 mm to 50 mm (Fig. 5e). This is a round wire nail having a very large flat head. Usually galvanised (dipped into molten zinc to prevent rusting), it is used for nailing down roofing felt, and fixing plaster board to ceiling joists.

### Cut tack

6 mm to 38 mm (Fig. 5f). This is used for fixing upholstery to wood.

Nails are sold by weight e.g. 2 kg (or 4 lb) of 50 mm round wire nails. Panel pins may be bought in smaller quantities, e.g. 125 g (or 4 oz) of 25 mm medium gauge steel panel pins.

Nailing, although a cheap and simple way of holding wood together, has certain disadvantages.

(a) Nails give an untidy finish to the job unless punched below the surface of the wood and 'stopped' (Fig. 6).

(b) Once hammered in, nails are difficult to remove without damaging the surrounding wood.

### Screwing

Screws (except when in end grain) make a much firmer and often neater fixing than nails, and have the additional advantage that they can be easily removed. Metal fittings such as hinges, catches and locks are screwed to wood. Fig. 7a shows a standard woodscrew with countersunk head; Fig. 7b to d show alternative types of head.

Woodscrews are usually made of mild steel, or brass (for use in hardwoods such as oak where steel would be corroded), but may be obtained in stainless steel, or gunmetal, or be chromium-plated or enamelled (japanned).

When screwing together two pieces of wood, a shank clearance hole must be bored through the first piece (X in Fig. 8a). A smaller 'pilot' or 'lead' hole is then made in the second piece (Y) to prevent splitting. This may be done with a fine drill or bradawl (Fig. 9). If the screw head is countersunk to fit flush with the surface of piece X, a countersink or rose bit (see Fig. 318) is used to make the recess for it (Fig. 8b).

Where the head is to be covered by a wooden plug (Fig. 8c) the larger diameter hole ('counter-bore') should be drilled first, then the shank clearance hole, and finally the lead hole in piece Y. After inserting the screw, the plug is glued in position and planed off flush with the surface of the wood.

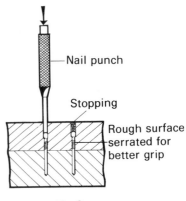

Fig. 6

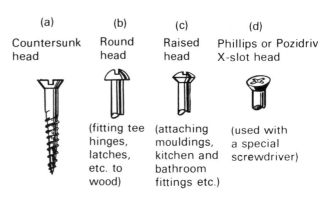

Fig. 7

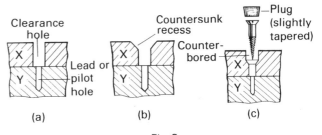

Fig. 8

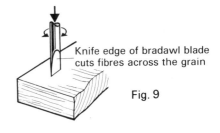

Fig. 9

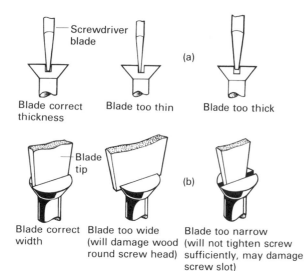

Blade correct thickness    Blade too thin    Blade too thick    (a)

Blade correct width    Blade too wide (will damage wood round screw head)    Blade too narrow (will not tighten screw sufficiently, may damage screw slot)    (b)

Fig. 10

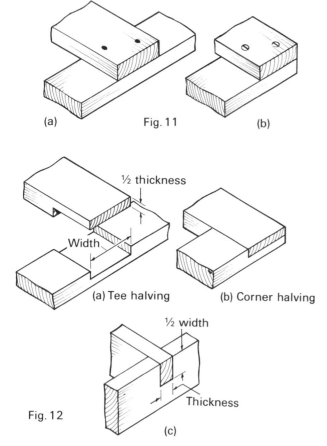

(a)    Fig. 11    (b)

½ thickness

Width

(a) Tee halving    (b) Corner halving

½ width

Thickness

Fig. 12    (c)

Care should be taken to use a screwdriver with a head which fits the screw slot correctly (Fig. 10a and b). Screws to be inserted into hardwoods can be screwed in more easily if their threads have previously been smeared with wax.

Woodscrews are not described by the measurement of their shank diameter, but by a gauge number ranging from 1 to 24. At the time of writing, a metric British Standard for woodscrews has not yet been produced. The existing imperial British Standard for woodscrews, BS 1210, gives metric equivalents. A No. 8 screw has a shank diameter of 4·2 mm, a No. 12 is 5·6 mm in diameter (the higher the number, the larger the shank diameter).

To order screws, give these details:

| *quantity* | *length* | *gauge* | *head* | *metal/finish* |
|---|---|---|---|---|
| 100 | 25 mm | 10 | round | chromium-plated brass. |

When wood has been nailed or screwed together, as in Fig. 11, it is said to be lap jointed.

## Halving joints

It is often neater to half lap (or halve) by cutting away half the thickness (or width) of each piece of wood (Fig. 12a to e), and a complete frame can be made using halving joints only (Fig. 13).

## Cross halving

Used for jointing rails which cross each other. (The general method of making this joint can be applied to other halving joints.)

Step 1 Prepare wood accurately to size.

Step 2 (a) Square across the grain (shoulders), using marking knife, try square, and ruler.
(b) Gauge along grain, using marking gauge set to half thickness (Fig. 14a).
(c) Mark the waste with a pencil.

Step 3 With a tenon saw, cut to the waste side of the lines and in the waste (to make chiselling easier), as in Fig. 14b.

Step 4 Chisel out waste in two stages, as in Fig. 14c and d. In each case, work from both edges towards the centre to avoid splitting off the far edge of the wood.

NOTE: *bevel on chisel blade should be uppermost when paring (smoothing off) the inside of the joint.*

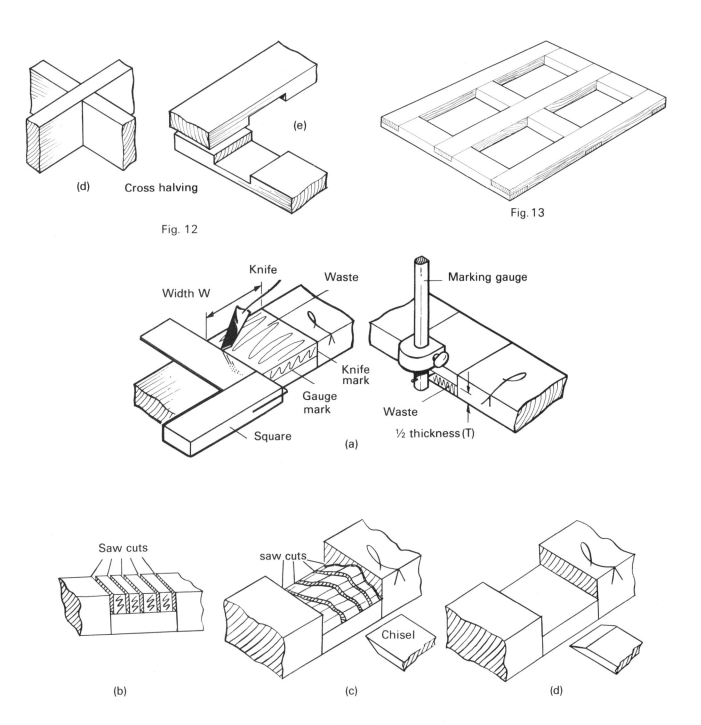

(d)  Cross halving

Fig. 12

Fig. 13

Width W    Knife    Waste

Knife mark

Gauge mark

Square

Marking gauge

Waste

½ thickness (T)

(a)

Saw cuts

saw cuts

Chisel

(b)                    (c)                    (d)

Fig. 14

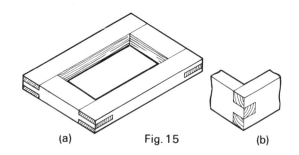

(a)    Fig. 15    (b)

A good cross halving or tee halving joint will hold together without nails, screws, or glue, but a corner halving (lap joint) will not. To overcome this difficulty a bridle joint may be used (Fig. 15a and b).

### Bridles

### Corner (open) bridle

Used for small simple frames.

Step 1  Fig. 16a shows the setting out. Note the extra 1 mm allowed for cleaning up (trimming) the joint (Fig. 16a).

Step 2  Saw to waste side of lines as in Fig. 16b, sawing down the grain first then across the shoulder lines to remove the waste. At the slot end, first bore a hole from each edge (Fig. 16c) and then saw down the cheek lines (Fig. 16d to f).

Step 3  Chisel out the waste by vertical paring from each edge (Fig. 16g).

Step 4  Fit the joint and trim off the 1 mm overhang with a smoothing plane, working in the direction of the arrows to avoid splitting the end grain (Fig. 16h).

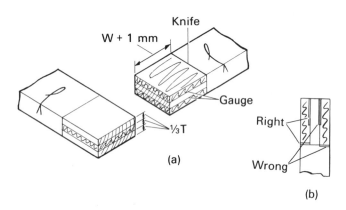

(a)    (b)

### Tee bridle (Fig. 17a)

Mark out as in Fig. 17b, cutting as instructed for corner bridle and cross halving joints. Fig. 17c shows a 'stopped' tee bridle used to joint a leg to the centre of a rail, and Fig. 17d an angled tee bridle.

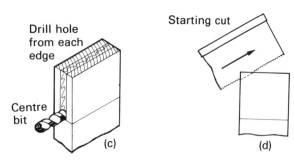

(c)    (d)

### Housing joints

Commonly used for fitting shelves into carcase ends. The groove or 'trenching' is gauged about one-third of the thickness of the wood in depth, and is either cut right across the wood (through housing, Fig. 18a), or stopped short of the front edge to give a neater appearance (stopped housing, Fig. 18b).

### Through housing

Fig. 19a shows the method of marking out and cutting. Fig. 19b illustrates the use of a guide strip which is often found useful. The saw blade is run against this guide to prevent overcutting the line.

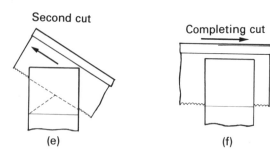

(e)    (f)

Fig. 16

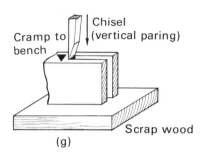

Cramp to bench

Chisel (vertical paring)

Scrap wood

(g)

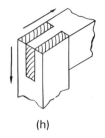

(h)

Fig. 16

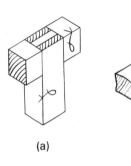

(a)

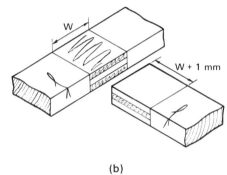

W

W + 1 mm

(b)

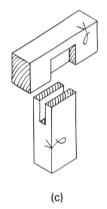

(c)

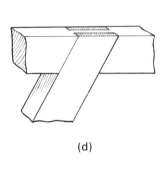

(d)

Fig. 17

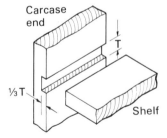

Carcase end

T

1/3 T

Shelf

10 mm

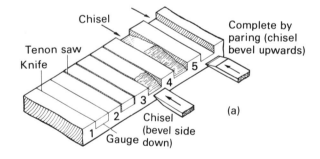

Chisel

Complete by paring (chisel bevel upwards)

Tenon saw

Knife

5

4

3

2

Chisel (bevel side down)

1

Gauge

(a)

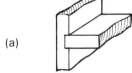

(a)

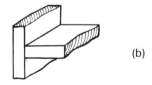

(b)

Fig. 18

(b)

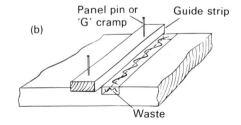

Panel pin or 'G' cramp

Guide strip

Waste

Fig. 19

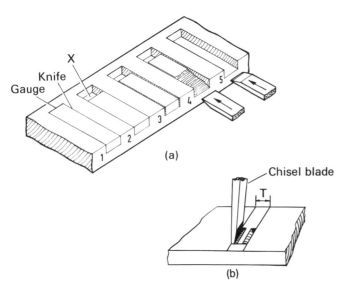

Fig. 20

## Stopped housing

Set out and cut the housing as in Fig. 20a. Difficulty will be found in cutting up to the closed end of the housing (X) as this part cannot be cut with the tenon saw. This end should first be carefully chiselled out as in Fig. 20b. The rest of the trenching may then be sawn and chiselled out. To complete (step 5), a router plane (see Fig. 306) may be used in addition to the chisel.

## Mortice and tenon

This is a framing joint (of which there are many types), used mainly in frame and stool construction (see Chapter 2).

## Through mortice and tenon

The general methods used to mark out and cut this basic joint should be applied to the other forms of mortice and tenon which follow.

Step 1 Square shoulder lines as in Fig. 21a.

Step 2 Set mortice gauge to the mortice chisel which is to be used (width of chisel about one-third of the thickness of the wood): e.g. 6 mm chisel for 18 mm thick wood.
(a) Slacken stock locking screw.
(b) Adjust spur points as in Fig. 21b.
(c) Slide stock along stem of gauge to give correct position of mortice and tighten stock locking screw (Fig. 21c).

Step 3 Gauge as in Fig. 21a and mark waste with a pencil.

Step 4 Saw tenon waste as for the corner bridle.

Step 5 (a) Chisel out the mortice, working from the centre towards each end (Fig. 21d and e). This will make chip removal easier. (Note position of chisel bevel.) Do not cut away the end 3 mm at this stage or the ends of the mortice will be burred over. When halfway through the wood, turn it over and cut through from the other edge. During step 5 the morticed piece should be cramped securely to the bench top, with a piece of scrap wood under the work to protect the bench and another smaller piece between the cramp jaw and the work itself to prevent any 'bruising' of the wood.

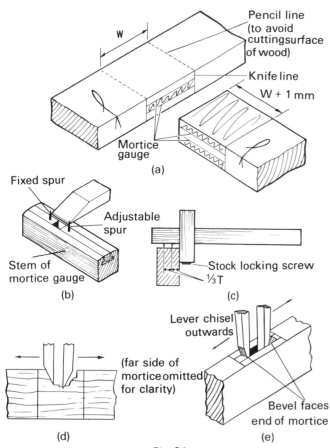

Fig. 21

(b) To 'square off' the ends of the mortice, hold the chisel as in Fig. 21f and g, levering inwards. Cut in this way from both edges of the wood. The sides of the mortice should not be chiselled or it will become too wide for the tenon.

When cutting large mortices, first drill out some of the waste with a brace and bit (Fig. 21h).

Step 6 After assembly, the 1 mm waste on the end of the tenon is smoothed off with a plane, giving a neat smooth finish to the joint (Fig. 21i).

Extra firmness in the joint may be obtained by wedging the tenon (Fig. 21j).

See also page 43.

## Stopped mortice and tenon

When for the sake of appearance the tenon is 'stopped' (Fig. 22a), the tenon is taken two-thirds of the way through the wood. Great care must be taken to ensure that the mortice is cut parallel to the sides. To avoid error the edge of the chisel blade should be 'sighted' against the edge of a try-square (Fig. 22b). Alternatively the edge of a steel rule should be held against the side of the wood and the chisel 'sighted' against it (Fig. 22c).

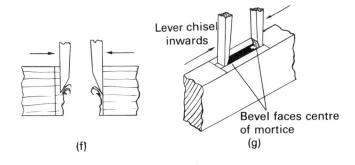

(f)

(g)

Lever chisel inwards

Bevel faces centre of mortice

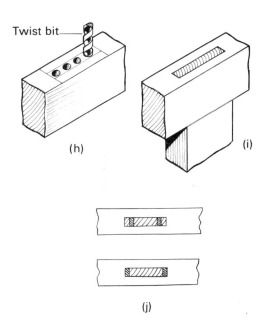

Twist bit

(h)

(i)

(j)

Fig. 21

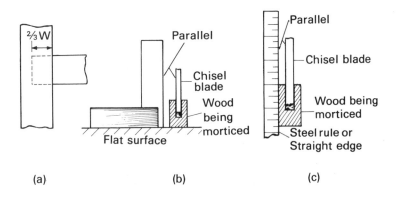

²/₃ W

Parallel

Chisel blade

Wood being morticed

Flat surface

Parallel

Chisel blade

Wood being morticed

Steel rule or Straight edge

(a)

(b)

(c)

Fig. 22

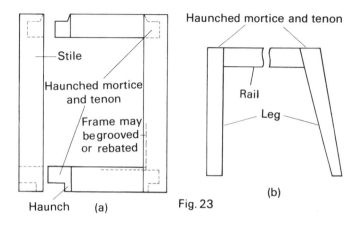

Haunched mortice and tenon

Fig. 23

## Haunched mortice and tenon

Used where the tenon fits into a mortice which is at or near the end of a leg or stile (vertical member of a frame) (Fig. 23a and b).

The tenon may be through or stopped, and the haunch either rectangular (square) or sloped (secret). A rectangular haunch provides greater joint strength, but the sloping haunch gives a neater joint where the finished appearance is of more importance. The haunch lessens the chances of the rail twisting after the job has been assembled, and prevents a gap showing between the tenon shoulder and the face of the morticed stile or leg, should any shrinkage take place.

## Stopped haunched mortice and tenon (Sloping haunch)

Step 1  Set out as in Fig. 24a, allowing at least 15 mm waste or 'horn' at the haunching end of the mortice. This strengthens the joint during cutting and assembly.

Step 2  Chisel the mortice $\frac{2}{3}$ width deep, and then cut sloping haunching at about 25° to 30° (Fig. 24b).

Step 3  Saw tenon cheeks, sloping haunch, and then the shoulders (Fig. 24c), and trim the haunch so that a good fit is obtained. If any adjustment to the tenon cheeks is required, this should be carried out with a chisel (by paring across the grain) or shoulder plane.

Some common faults are shown in Fig. 24e to g. In Fig. 24e, the mortice has not been chiselled parallel to the sides (see also Fig. 22b). Face the end of the mortice when chiselling, to see whether the chisel blade is vertical or not.

Fig. 24f shows one possible effect of a carelessly sawn tenon where the saw cut (kerf) has extended into the tenon and not remained on the waste side of the gauge mark. Fig. 24g shows faulty tenon shoulders, again the result of careless sawing.

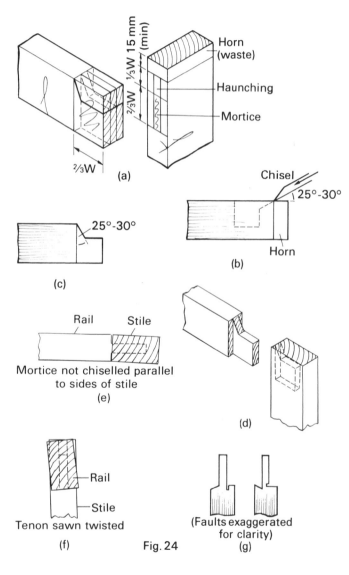

Fig. 24

**Rectangular haunched mortice and tenon**
The setting out of this is similar to that of the previous joint, except that the haunch is sawn square and the haunching chopped out to match it (Fig. 25). The tenon may be taken right through the stile.

**Haunched mortice and tenon for a grooved frame**
Where the inner edges of frame members are grooved to hold a panel (Fig. 26), a modified form of the rectangular haunched mortice and tenon joint is used (Fig. 27 a to c).

Step 1 Set out as for a simple haunched mortice and tenon, but measure up the depth of the groove from the inner end of the mortice – usually 6 mm to 10 mm, depending on the frame size.

Step 2 Cut the mortice, but leave the haunching.

Step 3 Groove with a plough plane (see Fig. 301) and then chisel out haunching to width of mortice and depth of groove. (Note: the groove should be positioned between the edges of the mortice.)
Some craftsmen prefer to carry out step 3 before step 2.

Step 4 Saw tenon cheeks, plough groove in rail, and saw shoulders. Cut a 'square' haunch to fill the haunching in the mortice. Trim away any waste at X.

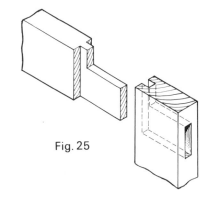

Fig. 25

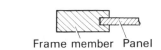

Frame member  Panel

Fig. 26

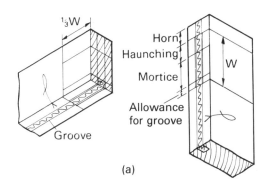

$\frac{1}{3}$W

Horn
Haunching
Mortice
W
Allowance for groove
Groove

(a)

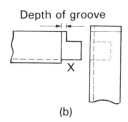

Depth of groove

X

(b)

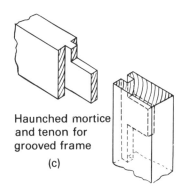

Haunched mortice and tenon for grooved frame

(c)

Fig. 27

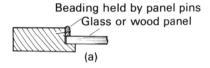

Beading held by panel pins
Glass or wood panel

(a)

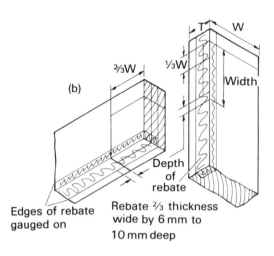

(b)

T  W

²⁄₃W    ⅓W    Width

Depth of rebate

Edges of rebate gauged on

Rebate ²⁄₃ thickness wide by 6 mm to 10 mm deep

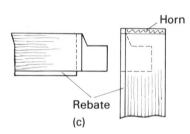

Horn

Rebate

(c)

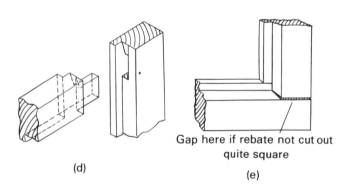

(d)

Gap here if rebate not cut out quite square

(e)

Fig. 28

**Haunched mortice and tenon for a rebated frame** (long and short shouldered)
Once a panel has been assembled into a grooved and glued-up frame it is impossible to remove it without damaging the frame. For this reason, where panels must be replaceable or where glass is to be fitted into the frame, the rebated (stepped) frame is used (Fig. 28a).

The basic joint must again be altered to allow for the rebate.

Step 1 Set out as in Fig. 28b. Notice the difference between this and the joint used for the grooved frame. The tenon is longer on the front (unrebated side) by the depth of rebate. It is usual to mark on the edges of the rebate with a cutting gauge. (Note: the edge of the rebate coincides with one edge of the mortice.)

Step 2 Cut the mortice and tenon cheeks.

Step 3 Cut rebate with a plough or rebate (rabbet) plane and then saw tenon shoulders.

Step 4 Make sloping haunching and trim haunch to fit (Fig. 28c) and complete as Fig. 28d. Care must be taken to keep the rebate quite square, or a gap will occur at the back shoulder (Fig. 28e).

**Forked tenon** (Fig. 29)
Used on wide rails, it prevents weakening of the stile or leg by long morticing; it is normally used for rails over 75 mm wide. Note that the lower edge of the tenon has been 'shouldered'. Should shrinkage take place across the rail, the shoulder prevents a gap from showing at the lower end of the mortice.

**Twin (double) mortice and tenon** (Fig. 30a)
Used where the width of a rail (e.g. a drawer rail) is such that one tenon is insufficient to prevent twisting. It may be combined with a housing joint for fitting wide shelves, etc. (Fig. 30b). It may be stopped if required.

**Bare-faced tenon**
Used where a rail is too thin to carry two shoulders without weakening the tenon (Fig. 31a). It may also be used in stool construction (Fig. 31b and c).

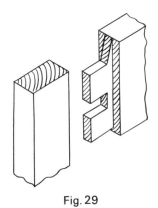

Fig. 29

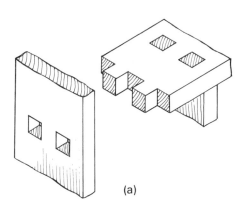

(a)

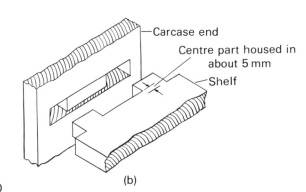

Carcase end

Centre part housed in
about 5 mm

Shelf

(b)

Fig. 30

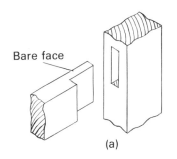

Bare face

(a)

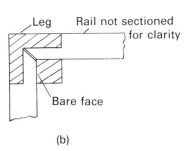

Leg    Rail not sectioned
for clarity

Bare face

(b)

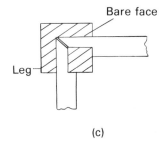

Bare face

Leg

(c)

Fig. 31

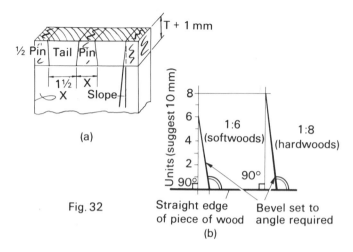

Fig. 32

(a)

(b)

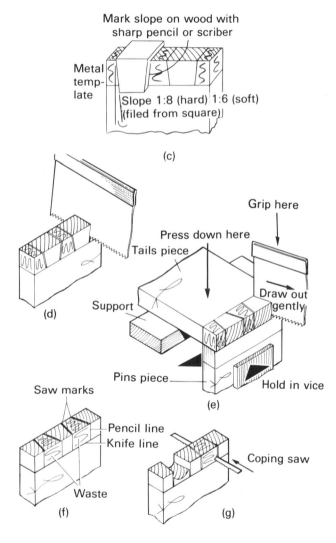

(c)

(d)

(e)

(f)

(g)

## Dovetails

### Through dovetail

Used for box and carcase construction.

Step 1 Square round shoulders of both the pins and the tail pieces at T + 1 mm from trued up ends, using a marking knife and try square.

Step 2 Draw in tails (Fig. 32a). The slope (1 : 8 for hardwoods, 1 : 6 for softwoods) is marked on in pencil using a dovetail template (Fig. 32c) or a try square and carpenter's adjustable bevel which has been set as in Fig. 32b. As shown in Fig. 32a, it is usual to have a half pin at each end of the joint. Tails are about $1\frac{1}{2}$ times the width of pins.

Step 3 Saw down the tails to shoulder lines using a fine tenon saw or dovetail saw (Fig. 32d).

Step 4 Mark through on to the end of the pins with the saw (Fig. 32e) and then square these marks down the sides to the shoulder line (Fig. 32f).

Step 5 Saw to waste side of pins (on pins piece) and then saw out most of the waste with a coping saw (Fig. 32g).

Step 6 Complete cutting by vertical paring using bevelled edge chisels. Cut half way through thickness from each side of the wood, cramping the work firmly on top of a piece of scrap wood (Fig. 32h). Be careful not to overcut the shoulder lines. The waste is removed from the tails piece in a similar way.

Step 7 Assemble, using light hammer blows and protecting the surface of the wood with a small piece of scrap wood. After gluing, trim off 1 mm overhang by planing in direction of arrows (Fig. 32i).

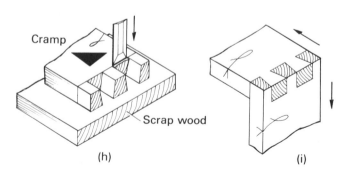

(h)

(i)

Some woodworkers prefer to complete the cutting of the tails first and to mark on the ends of the pins with a fine scriber (Fig. 33).

NOTE: *do not saw out the 'wrong' part of the joint. Do saw sides of pins quite parallel to the edges of the wood and tails square to the sides, or splitting is likely to occur on assembly.*

## Lap dovetail

Used for carcase and drawer construction (see pages 35–6).

Step 1 The ends of the wood must be 'shot' (planed) exactly square.

Step 2 Mark on shoulder lines, using a cutting gauge (Fig. 34a). A cutting gauge has a small knife-edged blade instead of a spur as on a marking gauge (see Fig. 269).

Step 3 Draw in tails and saw them as for a through dovetail.

Step 4 Mark pins from tails, using either the saw or scriber (Fig. 34b).

Step 5 Complete the cutting of the tails in the normal manner.

Step 6 Pins are partly sawn out (Fig. 34c); then with the work cramped to the bench the waste is cut out using bevelled edge chisels (Fig. 34d to f).

Step 7 Assemble as a through dovetail.

NOTE: *care must be taken to clean out all waste wood especially on the 'lap' part (X in Fig. 34f). Failure to do this will result in gaps – see Fig. 34g.*

For drawer-making very fine pins are used (Fig. 34h).

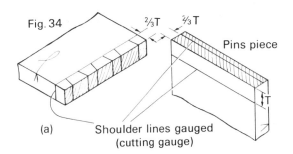

Fig. 34

$\frac{2}{3}$T    $\frac{2}{3}$T

Pins piece

T

(a)    Shoulder lines gauged (cutting gauge)

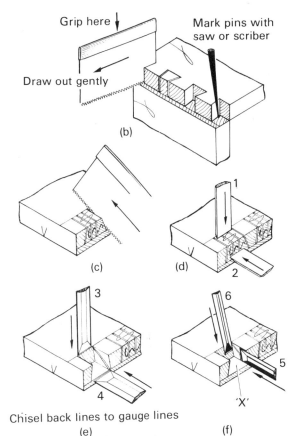

Grip here    Mark pins with saw or scriber

Draw out gently

(b)

(c)    (d)

1    2

3    6

5

4    'X'

Chisel back lines to gauge lines

(e)    (f)

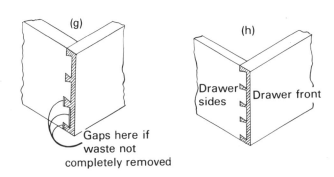

(g)    (h)

Gaps here if waste not completely removed

Drawer sides    Drawer front

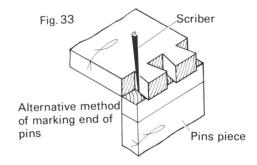

Fig. 33    Scriber

Alternative method of marking end of pins    Pins piece

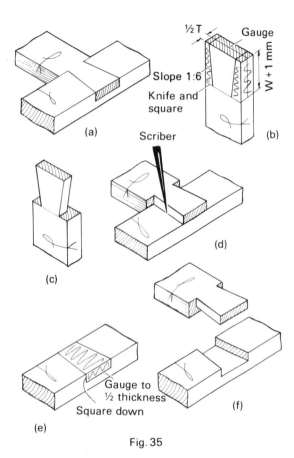

Fig. 35

## Dovetail tee-halving (Fig. 35a)

Used in place of the standard tee-halving (Fig. 12a) where greater strength is needed.

Step 1 Set out tail as in Fig. 35b, following the instructions already given.

Step 2 Complete tail by sawing down gauge lines, across shoulders, and down slopes of tail (Fig. 35c).

Step 3 Stand tail in position on cross rail and scribe round it, using a very fine knife blade or scriber (Fig. 35d).

Step 4 Square down from these marks to gauge mark (set at half thickness): see Fig. 35e.

Step 5 Saw to waste side of lines, and complete by chiselling out (Fig. 35f).

## Edge joints

Used to produce wide boards (e.g. table tops). The grain in all pieces must run in the same direction, otherwise planing up after gluing will be very difficult. Notice also the arrangement of 'end grain'. Through and through ('slash') sawn timber should have the 'heart' side on alternate faces (Fig. 36a), and quarter sawn stock should be assembled as in Fig. 36b. Each joint should be marked with a pencil for easy reference.

## Rubbed butt joint

Though theoretically very easy to make, this joint requires much care and practice for successful completion.

Step 1 The edges to be jointed are planed dead true with a trying plane (see Fig. 299b). One board is gripped in a vice and the other is rested on top of it. No light should be seen anywhere through the joint and it should be checked for flatness (Fig. 37a). Possible errors are shown in Fig. 37b and c.

Step 2 Place one board in the vice, apply glue to both meeting edges, and put second board in position, rubbing it backwards and forwards until it becomes too stiff to move (Fig. 37d).

NOTE: *fresh, hot animal glue should be used. The joint should not be cramped while setting, but either left in the vice or supported on edge – see Fig. 37 e.*

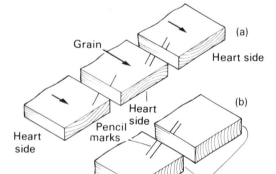

Fig. 36

If synthetic resin glues are used the joint should not be rubbed but cramped during the setting period.

### Tongued and grooved joint (Fig. 38)
Used widely for floor boarding (with fixed tongue worked from the solid). If glued and cramped until set, it is an alternative to rubbed, dowelled, or slot-screwed butt joints. Loose tongues are made from strips of cross-grained wood or plywood.

### Slot-screwed butt joint
A reinforced butt joint, also used for fitting strip-type door and drawer handles (see Fig. 151d).

Step 1 Prepare, but do not glue, a rubbed butt joint.

Step 2 At suitable distances along the length, square across the meeting edges as in Fig. 39a.

Step 3 Drill holes $X_1$ and $X_2$ in piece B, large enough to clear the screw heads which are inserted into piece A ($Y_1$, $Y_2$), until about 6 mm or 8 mm of shank remains visible. The holes are slotted keyhole fashion with a chisel just wider than the screw shank diameter (Fig. 39b), and the joint is assembled by tapping piece B in the direction of the arrow. The screw heads undercut the chiselled slots, thus giving a grip (Fig. 39c).

Step 4 The joint is then taken apart and the screws tightened an extra quarter of a turn. Apply glue to both edges and re-assemble. (Animal or synthetic glues may be used for this joint.)

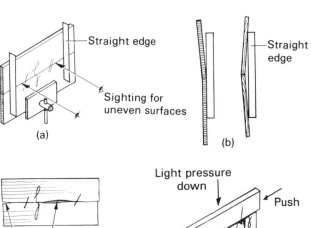

Straight edge

Sighting for uneven surfaces

(a)

Straight edge

(b)

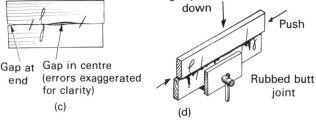

Gap at end

Gap in centre (errors exaggerated for clarity)

(c)

Light pressure down

Push

Rubbed butt joint

(d)

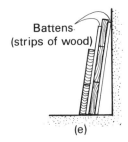

Battens (strips of wood)

(e)

Fig. 37

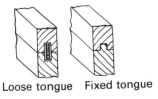

Loose tongue    Fixed tongue

Fig. 38

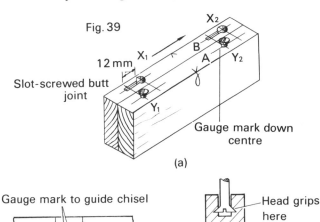

Fig. 39

$X_2$

$X_1$

B

A

$Y_2$

12 mm

Slot-screwed butt joint

$Y_1$

Gauge mark down centre

(a)

Gauge mark to guide chisel

(b) Centre line (gauged)

Head grips here

(c)

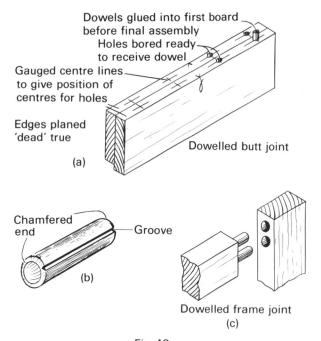

Dowels glued into first board before final assembly

Holes bored ready to receive dowel

Gauged centre lines to give position of centres for holes

Edges planed 'dead' true

(a)

Dowelled butt joint

Chamfered end — Groove

(b)

Dowelled frame joint

(c)

Fig. 40

## Dowelled butt joint

Board edges may be dowelled together.

Step 1 Prepare, but do not glue, a rubbed butt joint.

Step 2 Square across edges and gauge to half thickness (Fig. 40a).

Step 3 Drill holes with a Jennings or similar type of bit (see Fig. 316) to a depth of rather more than half the length of the dowel. The dowels should be grooved to allow glue to escape past them when they are inserted into the holes, and their ends should be chamfered for easy insertion (Fig. 40b).

Step 4 Glue dowels and edges, assemble joint and cramp until set. Dowels may also be used instead of mortice and tenon joints; usually two or three dowels replace each tenon (Fig. 40c)'

When dowels are used in this way, a simple metal dowelling jig or template is useful (Fig. 41a). Care must be taken to ensure that the holes are bored quite square to the joint face (Fig. 41b).

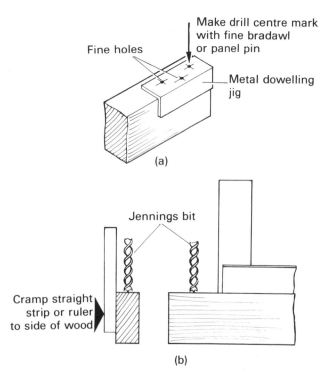

Make drill centre mark with fine bradawl or panel pin

Fine holes

Metal dowelling jig

(a)

Jennings bit

Cramp straight strip or ruler to side of wood

(b)

Fig. 41

# 2 Constructions

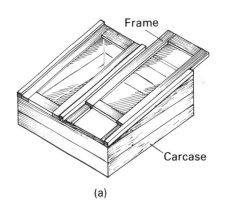

(a)

The three basic forms of construction used in joinery and cabinet making are *flat frame*: e.g. a door or window frame (Fig. 42a); *stool*: e.g. a table or chair (Fig. 42b); and *box* or *carcase*: e.g. the main part of a wardrobe, chest of drawers, or tool box (Fig. 42c).

Many jobs involve combining two or more of these constructions – for instance, a garden frame consists of a carcase with two or more sliding or hinged 'lights' (window frames) (Fig. 43a). A cupboard is a carcase fitted with doors (flat frames) and may stand on a stool (Fig. 43b).

(b)

Fig. 43

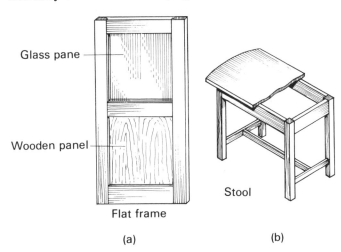

(a)

(b)

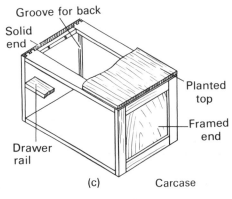

(c)     Carcase

Fig. 42

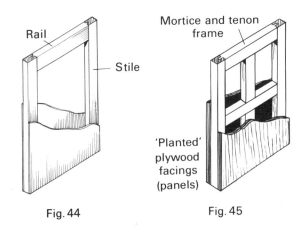

Fig. 44        Fig. 45

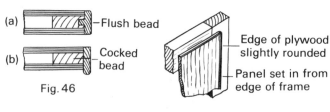

(a) — Flush bead

(b) — Cocked bead

Fig. 46

Edge of plywood slightly rounded

Panel set in from edge of frame

Fig. 47

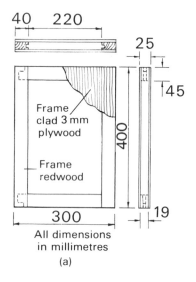

Frame clad 3 mm plywood

Frame redwood

All dimensions in millimetres

(a)

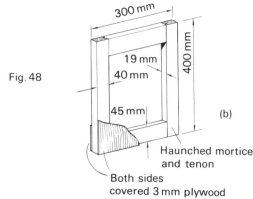

Fig. 48

300 mm

19 mm
40 mm

400 mm

45 mm

(b)

Haunched mortice and tenon

Both sides covered 3 mm plywood

| Door | | | | Name | | |
|------|------|------|------|------|------|------|
| PART | N°off | L. | W. | Th. | WOOD | REMARKS. |
| Stiles | 2 | 425 | 40 | 19 | European Redwood | extra 25mm for horns |
| Rails | 2 | 275 | 45 | 19 | " | |
| Panels | 2 | 405 | 305 | .3 | Birch Plywood | left oversize for trimming |
| All sizes nett ( planed ) in millimetres | | | | | | |

Fig. 49

## FLAT FRAME CONSTRUCTION

Depending upon how it is to be used on completion, a frame may be jointed together in a number of different ways. Fig. 13 and 15a show simple ways of making a frame. Where a neater appearance and greater strength are necessary (e.g. when making doors and windows), various forms of the mortice and tenon joint are usually employed.

A simple 'flush' door (Fig. 44) can be made by sandwiching a plain haunched mortice and tenon jointed frame between two sheets of plywood or hardboard. On larger doors of this type extra stiffness is obtained by fitting additional horizontal and/or vertical rails which are stop tenoned into the outer frame (Fig. 45). The edges of the plywood may be protected and hidden by lipping as in Fig. 46.

Alternatively, the edges of the plywood or hardboard panels may be trimmed, rounded off and set in a little way from the edge of the frame (Fig. 47).

To make up a small flush panelled door similar to that shown in Fig. 44, follow these steps.

Step 1 *Drawing*

First prepare a drawing showing how the job is to be made. If the job is a simple construction, the drawing need not always be to scale (as in Fig. 48a); often a pictorial sketch (see Fig. 48b) is sufficient. Whatever form of drawing is used, it must show:
(a) the overall (outside) dimensions (measurements) of the object;
(b) the dimensions of all pieces of timber used in making it;
(c) the method of construction (joints, etc.) used.
(Further information on drawing and design is given in Chapter 11.)

Step 2 *Cutting list*

From the working drawing or dimensioned sketch, draw up a list of all the parts together with their dimensions (Fig. 49). The sizes given are 'finished' or prepared sizes, with the exception of the stiles where extra length is allowed for the horns. In this example the panels too are sawn a little oversize.

When marking out on the board before
rough sawing (see Fig. 2), allowances are
made to cater for sawing and planing to size:

length     – add 15 mm
width      – add 7 mm to 9 mm
thickness – add 4 mm to 5 mm.

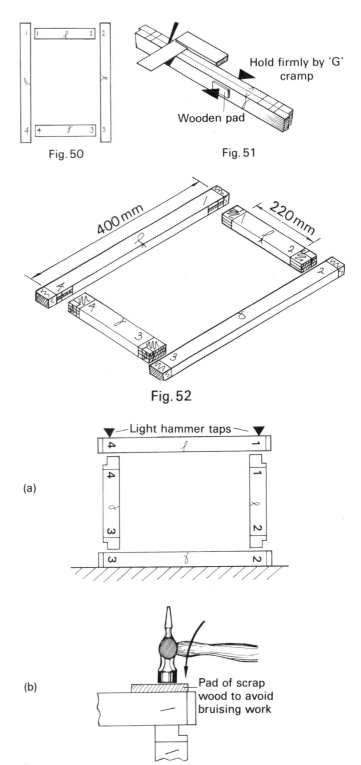

Fig. 50

Fig. 51

Hold firmly by 'G' cramp

Wooden pad

Fig. 52

400 mm

220 mm

Light hammer taps

(a)

(b)

Pad of scrap wood to avoid bruising work

Fig. 53

Step 3 *Setting out* (arrangement and marking out of joints)

(a) After sawing and planing to size, lay out
the parts of the frame in their exact positions
and note and number off the positions of the
joints (e.g. tenon number 2 to fit mortice
number 2). Face sides are kept to one side of
the frame with the face edges inwards (Fig.
50). (In some jobs there may be reasons for
having the face edges outwards.)

(b) Cramp the two stiles together, using one
or two G cramps, and square the lines for the
ends of the mortices across both at the same
time (Fig. 51). This prevents accidental
variations in distances between joints, etc.,
and saves time as well. Mark the positions of
the tenon shoulders on the rail, and cramp
them together in a similar way. Each shoulder
line should then be squared round as
required.

(c) Gauge the mortices and tenons, setting
the mortice gauge to a 6 mm mortice chisel.

(d) Mark all waste with a pencil.

(e) Lay out all the parts in their correct
positions again, and CHECK all numbers,
measurements, shoulder lines and gauge
marks (Fig. 52). Think twice before you cut
once.

Step 4 *Cutting*

Saw and chisel the joints as described on
pages 10–13.

Step 5 *Assembly*

(a) Assemble and check the fit of each joint
individually. When all are satisfactory,
assemble the complete frame (Fig. 53a and b).

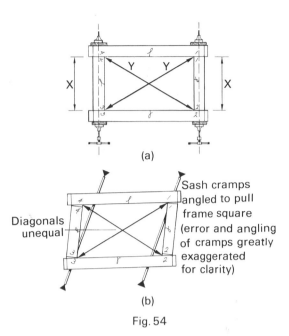

(a)

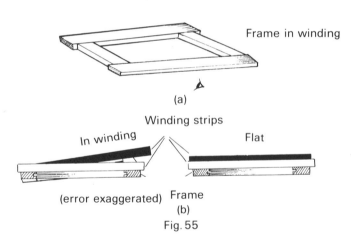

Diagonals unequal

Sash cramps angled to pull frame square (error and angling of cramps greatly exaggerated for clarity)

(b)

Fig. 54

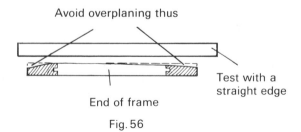

Frame in winding

(a)

Winding strips

In winding     Flat

(error exaggerated)  Frame
(b)
Fig. 55

Avoid overplaning thus

Test with a straight edge

End of frame

Fig. 56

(b) After assembling, apply further pressure by means of sash cramps to tighten the joints fully, using small pads of scrap wood between the cramp jaws and the work to prevent bruising (Fig. 54a).

NOTE: *the cramps must lie along the centre line of the rails (as in Fig. 54a) and the rails should be tight against the bars of the cramps. This will prevent the frame from being pulled out of true. Should the frame be found to be a little out of true, a slight alteration to the position of the cramps may enable it to be pulled square (Fig. 54b). (If the frame returns to an out-of-square shape when the cramps are removed, some adjustment to the joints or shoulder lengths is required.)*

Step 6 *Checking*

Check shoulder lengths X and diagonals Y (Fig. 54a) to ensure squareness, and 'sight' the frame as in Fig. 55 to check that the rails and stiles are not 'in winding' (twisted). 'Winding strips' (trued pairs of wood or metal strips used in checking for wind when planing timber) are sometimes useful (Fig. 55b).

Step 7 *Gluing up*

If, after assembling and checking 'dry' (without glue), the frame is found quite true in all respects, it should be taken apart, adhesive applied to both parts of each joint, and re-assembled. Cramp up again and *re-check very carefully*. Remember that once the adhesive has set, errors cannot be rectified. Wipe off any surplus adhesive and leave to set. The setting time needed before the frame can be cleaned up will depend upon the type of adhesive used (see Chapter 3).

Step 8 *Cleaning up*

(a) Saw off the horns at each end of the stiles, using a tenon saw.
(b) With a *fine* set smoothing plane, level off both faces (sides) of each joint, checking with a straight edge to ensure that a flat surface is maintained across the frame. Avoid errors such as are shown in Fig. 56.
(c) Check one edge of the frame using a straight edge and try-square, adjusting with a fine set plane if necessary.

(d) Check and adjust the opposite long edge of the frame.

(e) Plane the end grain of the stiles, being careful not to split off the corners, and give a final skim to the ends of the frame, again checking with try-square, rule and straight-edge.

NOTE: *if the frame is to be covered with plywood or hardboard as in Fig. 44, do not carry out steps 8c, d, or e until* after *the panels have been fitted to both sides of the frame.*

Step 9 *Fitting panels*

(a) Mark the outline of the frame in pencil on the underside (inside) of each panel (Fig. 57a). This will show exactly where to apply adhesive to the panels (Fig. 57b).

(b) Apply a suitable adhesive (see Chapter 3) to the faces of the frame and corresponding parts of the panels and assemble.

(c) Apply pressure evenly over the frame by means of strips of wood and G cramps (Fig. 58), a veneer press, or any other convenient means, and leave until set.

If a contact (impact) adhesive is used, then the edges may be trimmed immediately after assembly. This is a convenient way to fix panels of this type.

(d) Trim the edge of the panels and frame as suggested in stages 8c, d and e.

Step 10 *Lipping*

If required, the door may be lipped on all four edges if it is to be polished, or on only the top and opening edges if it is to be painted (Fig. 59a and b). The strips of lipping are individually cut to size and glued in position, a few panel pins being inserted where necessary to hold them in place until set. The pins may then be punched home or pulled out and the holes 'stopped'.

NOTE: *When making a door to fit into a carcase, it is usual to allow an extra 1 mm to 2 mm in width and length to allow for fitting. If lippings are to be used, they must be allowed for when calculating the dimensions of the frame.*

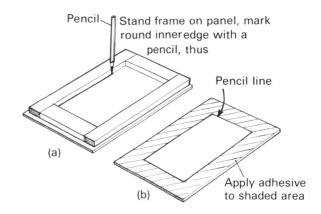

Pencil

Stand frame on panel, mark round inner edge with a pencil, thus

Pencil line

(a)

Apply adhesive to shaded area

(b)

Fig. 57

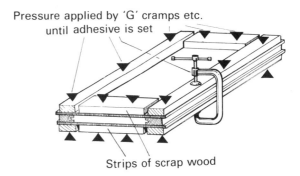

Pressure applied by 'G' cramps etc. until adhesive is set

Strips of scrap wood

Fig. 58

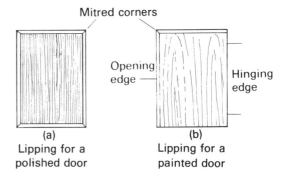

Mitred corners

Opening edge

Hinging edge

(a)
Lipping for a polished door

(b)
Lipping for a painted door

Fig. 59

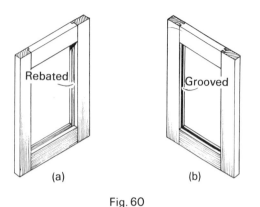

Fig. 60

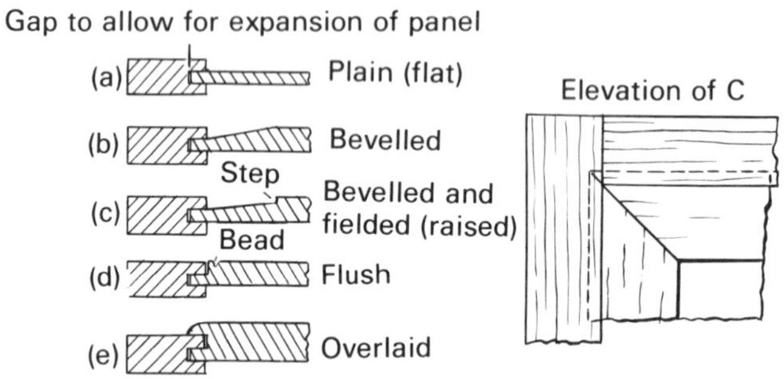

Gap to allow for expansion of panel

(a) Plain (flat)

(b) Bevelled

Step

(c) Bevelled and fielded (raised)

Bead

(d) Flush

(e) Overlaid

Elevation of C

Fig. 61

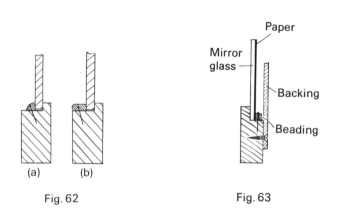

Fig. 62

Paper

Mirror glass

Backing

Beading

Fig. 63

## Doors with panels fitting in grooves or rebates

For painted cupboard doors (e.g. kitchen cupboards), or for veneered flush doors, the planted panel method has much to recommend it, but it cannot be used where a panel of solid wood is to be fitted. Solid wood will swell when damp and expand across the grain, shrinking again as it dries. It must, therefore, be allowed to 'move' or it will split.

Traditionally, panels are either grooved or rebated into the frame (Fig. 60a and b), a grooved frame usually being used for permanent panelling, and a rebated frame where the panel might need replacement (e.g. a mirror or glazed door).

When a solid wooden panel is used, it is often too thick to fit into the groove in the frame, so its thickness is reduced at the edges to make it a sliding fit in the grooved frame. Fig. 61 shows a number of ways of doing this, most of which give a decorative effect.

Panels are never glued into the grooves as allowance has to be made for expansion and contraction of the timber (see Chapter 8).

Where a glass panel (pane) is used, it is held in the rebate by beading (Fig. 62a and b) which itself is fixed to the frame by panel pins.

The 'silvering' on the back of mirror glass is easily scratched; to prevent damage to it a backing is fitted (see Fig. 63).

## Making a grooved or rebated frame

The method of making grooved or rebated frames is similar in outline to that already described (pages 22–5), but the following points should be noted.

(a)  The correct type of haunched mortice and tenon should be used: 'square' haunched for grooved frames (Fig. 25), and long and short shouldered for rebated frames (Fig. 28).

(b)  The panel of a grooved frame should be prepared and its fit checked before gluing the frame. Slight clearance all round the edges of the panel should be allowed.

(c)  As the grooved frame panel must be fitted at the time the frame is glued up, any cleaning up and polishing of the panel and inner edges of the framing should be done before final assembly.

## STOOL CONSTRUCTION

Fig. 64 shows a basic form of stool construction consisting of two end frames connected by top and bottom (stretcher) rails. Haunched mortice and tenon joints are used at the top of the legs, and plain mortices and tenons where the stretcher rails meet the legs and/or each other.

Many variations of this basic construction are possible (Fig. 65a to f). Fig. 66a to c shows methods of stool construction using tee-bridle, halving, and dovetail joints. Fig. 67a shows how the ends of tenons are mitred as in corner X, Fig. 64. If they were not mitred, one tenon would need to be shortened which would give a weaker joint (Fig. 67b).

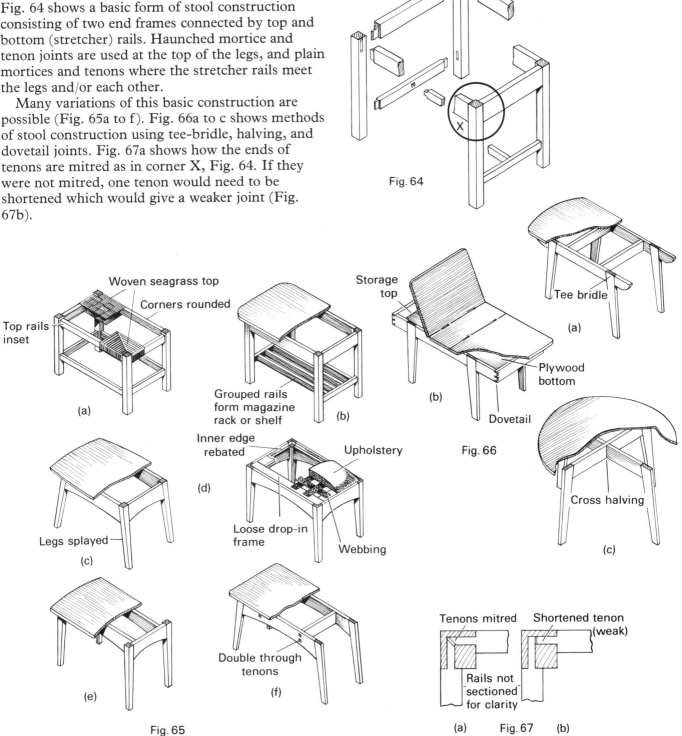

Fig. 64

(a) Top rails inset · Woven seagrass top · Corners rounded

(b) Grouped rails form magazine rack or shelf

(c) Legs splayed

(d) Inner edge rebated · Upholstery · Loose drop-in frame · Webbing

(e)

(f) Double through tenons

Fig. 65

(a) Tee bridle

(b) Storage top · Plywood bottom · Dovetail

(c) Cross halving

Fig. 66

Fig. 67 (a) Tenons mitred · Rails not sectioned for clarity    (b) Shortened tenon (weak)

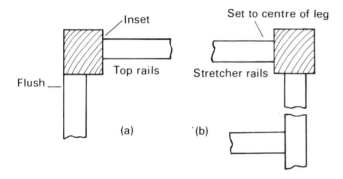

Fig. 68

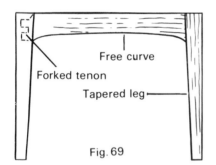

Fig. 69

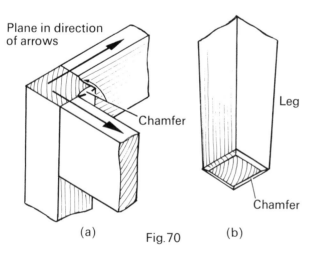

Fig. 70

Top rails are set either flush to or slightly in from the outside edges of the legs (Fig. 68a); stretchers are generally set in the middle of the thickness of the leg (Fig. 68b).

Where stretchers are left out (Fig. 65c to f), a wider top rail must be used to withstand the extra strain which will be put on the joints. To reduce the apparent width of the wider top rail its underside may be curved. If used with tapered legs, a very pleasing effect is obtained (Fig. 69 and 65d).

Chamfering (see Chapter 4) also produces a somewhat similar effect.

Several methods of fitting the tops of tables and stools are described in Chapter 3, pages 44–7.

Whatever the final form of stool construction, the method of making it will largely follow the lines suggested for the making of a flat frame (see pages 22–6).

Step 1 Make a fully detailed and dimensioned drawing of the job, showing all constructions, etc.

Step 2 Prepare a cutting list from the drawing.

Step 3 Prepare timber to size, set out and check arrangement of all the joints (as far as possible), marking the waste before cutting them.

Step 4 Cut and fit each joint.

Step 5 Cramp up and check the fit of each joint.

Step 6 Assemble dry, cramp up and check each end frame; then assemble, cramp up and check the whole stool. Take stool apart.

Step 7 Glasspaper each part of the stool where it cannot conveniently be cleaned up and smoothed after glueing, i.e. stretcher rails and inside edges of the legs. It is often an advantage to polish these parts before glueing because (a) the polish prevents adhesive sticking to the wood, and it can therefore be removed more easily; (b) polishing can be more easily carried out before the parts are permanently assembled.

Step 8 (a) Glue up, cramp and check each end frame, wiping off surplus adhesive before it sets.
(b) When both end frames have set, assemble the whole stool dry, cramp up and check again.

(c) Dismantle and glue the side rails to the end frames. Cramp, check and remove surplus adhesive.

Step 9 Clean up the outside as required, saw off and trim any horns, chamfering the inner edges of the top of the legs before planing the end grain (Fig. 70a).

Step 10 Level off the bottom of the legs if required, and chamfer them to prevent chipping during use (Fig. 70b).

Step 11 Glasspaper all unfinished surfaces and polish (see Chapter 7).

NOTE: (a) *The sharp edges of the top rails of stools with woven tops (seagrass or cord) should be rounded to prevent wear on the seagrass during use (Fig. 71).*

(b) *Wooden tops to stools or tables should be fitted as shown in Chapter 3. This may require some additional work to be carried out before final assembly.*

(c) *If the legs are splayed as in Fig. 65f or 66c, difficulty will be found in cramping. Either the cramp will tend to slip sideways (towards top of legs), thus opening out the bottom of the legs still further, or it will not pull the joints up tightly (Fig. 72a and b). To avoid this difficulty, a tapered pad is glued to the top of each leg, a piece of paper being inserted between it and the leg (Fig. 72c). When this is set the stool may be glued and cramped in the normal way, the wedge-shaped pad being removed when final cleaning up takes place.*

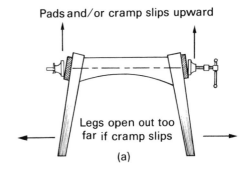

(a)

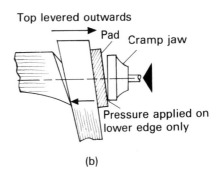

(b)

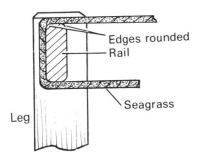

Fig. 71

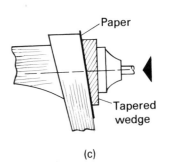

(c)

Fig. 72

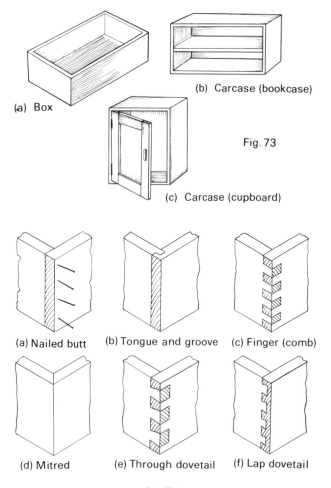

(a) Box

(b) Carcase (bookcase)

Fig. 73

(c) Carcase (cupboard)

(a) Nailed butt    (b) Tongue and groove    (c) Finger (comb)

(d) Mitred    (e) Through dovetail    (f) Lap dovetail

Fig. 74

Tongued and grooved (flush)    Rebated    Tongued and grooved (overlaid)

Fig. 75

Overhung    Inset

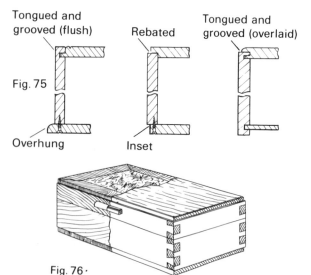

Fig. 76·

## CARCASE CONSTRUCTION

A carcase is basically a box stood on its end or side. (The bottom of the box then becomes the back.) If shelves are fitted, a simple bookcase is produced; the addition of a door turns the carcase into a cupboard (Fig. 73a, b and c).

### Boxes

Fig. 74a to f show several ways of jointing the sides of a box, the dovetail (Fig. 74e) being the strongest. Fig. 75 indicates ways of attaching the top and bottom to a box.

A small veneered box such as that shown in Fig. 76 would be made like this.

Step 1  *Drawing*

Prepare a detailed drawing giving all sizes and constructions (Fig. 77a). Indicate materials (type of wood, etc.) to be used (see Chapter 11).

Step 2  *Cutting list*

From the drawing, prepare a cutting list (Fig. 78).

Step 3  *Setting out (sides)*

(a) After preparing each piece of wood to its correct size, lay out and number the box sides as in Fig. 79a.

(b) Square across shoulder lines in pairs to ensure accuracy of shoulder length (Fig. 79b), and then square each shoulder right round. As this box has a 'well' lid (part of the box sides being sawn off to form the sides of the lid), gauge a line 15 mm down from the top edge on the outside face of each side piece (Fig. 79c).

(c) Mark out the tails at both ends of one long side, allowing one complete tail for the well lid. Notice that the pin which is later sawn in half is rather wider than usual to allow for the sawing and planing to fit (Fig. 77b).

Veneered box
(third angle orthographic projection)

Cross section
through handle

Half plan,
top removed

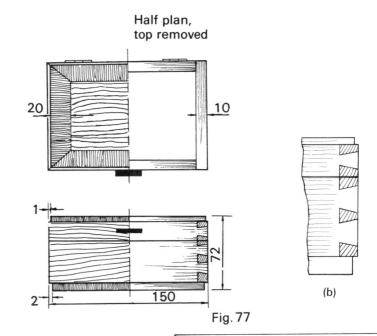

Fig. 77

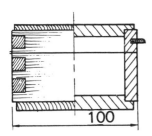

(a)

All dimensions in millimetres
Wood — Mahogany
Handle — Ebony
Veneers (sides and top) — Mahogany
Cross banding and plinth — Rosewood

Fig. 78

| Veneered box | | | | | | |
|---|---|---|---|---|---|---|
| Part | No.of | L | W | T | Wood | Remarks |
| Sides | 2 | 152 | 60 | 10 | Mahogany | Ends planed square |
| Ends | 2 | 102 | 60 | 10 | " | " |
| Top | 1 | 150 | 100 | 10 | " | " |
| Bottom | 1 | 150 | 100 | 12 | " | " |
| Handle | 1 | 30 | 10 | 3 | Ebony | " |
| All finished sizes in millimetres | | | | | | |

(a)

Knife mark   (c)   Gauge mark

Thickness + 1 mm
(b)

Fig. 79

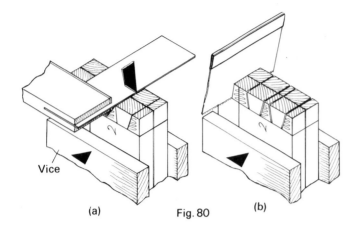

Vice

(a)          Fig. 80          (b)

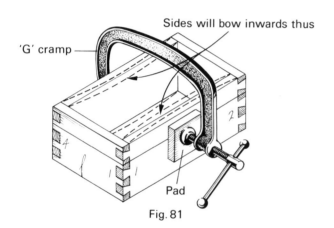

Sides will bow inwards thus

'G' cramp

Pad

Fig. 81

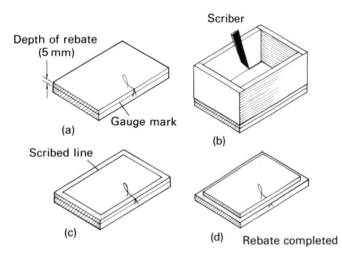

Depth of rebate
(5 mm)

Gauge mark

(a)

Scriber

(b)

Scribed line

(c)

(d)   Rebate completed

Fig. 82

(d) Cramp both long sides together in a vice and square across the end grain from the tail marks previously marked on the front (Fig. 80a). Mark in the waste.

Step 4   *Cutting*
Saw down tails on both pieces at the same time (Fig. 80b). Complete and check the fit of the joints in the usual way.

Step 5   *Assembly*
Assemble sides of box and cramp. Avoid applying pressure as in Fig. 81, as this will cause the sides to bow inwards.

Step 6   *Checking*
Ensure that the shoulders fit tightly together, measuring them and the diagonals as previously described to ensure that the box sides are 'square'.

Step 7   *Gluing*
(a) Before gluing, take sides apart and carefully glasspaper their inner faces using O grade glasspaper. If polishing is required, these inner faces should be polished before assembly.
(b) Glue and check in the normal way. Be sure to remove all surplus adhesive from the inside corners.

Step 8   *Cleaning up*
When set, clean up the outsides and edges with a smoothing plane. Do *not* overplane the corners, and take particular care to level the top and bottom edges accurately.

Step 9   *Setting out top and bottom*
(a) Ensure that the top and bottom are the same length and width as the box sides.
(b) Gauge depth of rebate from inner face of top and bottom (Fig. 82a).
(c) Stand sides on bottom (and top) and scribe round inner face of sides as in Fig. 82b to give exact inside dimensions (Fig. 82c). (If the sides have been accurately jointed the scribed lines should be parallel to each other and to the edges.)

Step 10   *Cutting*
Cut away the rebates, using rebate (rabbet) and shoulder planes along the grain. Across the grain (end rebates), first saw as for a

through housing, and then complete with rebate and shoulder planes (Fig. 82d).

Step 11 *Assembly*

The top and bottom should fit firmly in the sides, but should not be overtight.

(a) Cramp top and bottom in position, using large pads to spread the pressure evenly over the edges (Fig. 83). Adjust rebates if necessary so that a close fit is obtained.

(b) The edges and ends of the top and bottom should then be planed down to form the small external rebates shown in Fig. 77.

Step 12 *Gluing*

Smooth (and polish if required) the inner faces of top and bottom, apply adhesive to joint faces, re-assemble, and cramp until set (Fig. 83).

Step 13 *Veneering*

If veneering is required, this should be done next. (Instructions are given in Chapter 4, pages 56–60.)

Step 14 *'Opening' the box*

Put the box in the vice, and saw along the gauge line (regauged if the box has been veneered). First saw each corner as in Fig. 84a, then join up the cuts (Fig. 84b). Level the sawn surfaces with a smoothing plane set very finely. Remove as little wood as possible to obtain a fit free from gaps or corner wobble.

Step 15 *The handle*

Mark out and chisel a slot 25 mm × 3 mm in the centre of one side of the lid to take the handle. After fitting it, 'ease' the top edge and glue into place (Fig. 85).

Step 16 *Hinging*

Fit a pair of 25 mm brass butt hinges, as shown in Chapter 3, pages 49–50.

Step 17 *Polishing*

Suitable finishes are described in Chapter 7 (Fig. 222).

NOTE: *It will be seen from the foregoing that the general order of procedure in carrying out a job in wood is to all intents the same whatever the job is – drawing, cutting list, setting out, etc.*

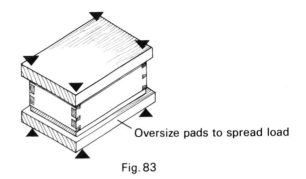

Oversize pads to spread load

Fig. 83

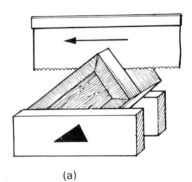

(a)

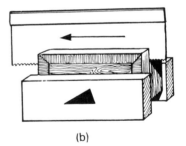

(b)

Fig. 84

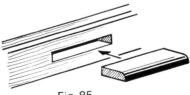

Fig. 85

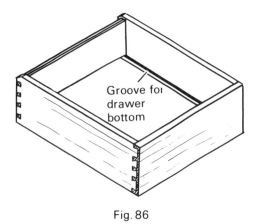

Fig. 86

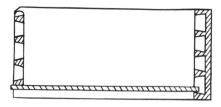

Fig. 87

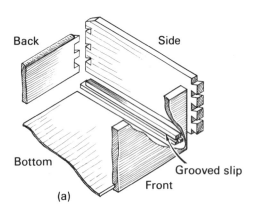

Back

Side

Bottom

Grooved slip

Front

(a)

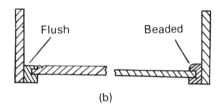

Flush

Beaded

(b)

Fig. 88

## Drawers

The traditional method of drawer construction is shown in Fig. 86 and 87; the drawer bottom is held in a groove in the drawer sides and front, passing under the back of the drawer as it is slid into position. But, as grooving the sides of the drawer weakens them, a better way of fitting the bottom is to use drawer slips (Fig. 88a and b), which are glued to the inner faces of the drawer sides and are tongued into the groove in the drawer front. This arrangement not only prevents weakening of the sides, but also gives a greater bearing surface on the drawer runners (supporting rails fitted to the carcase).

## Drawer-making

A drawer is a special kind of box and requires considerable care in making to ensure a good sliding fit in the carcase.

Step 1 *Preparation*

Prepare the drawer parts as follows:

*Sides:* Width – a tight push fit between the carcase runners

Thickness – usually between 6 mm and 10 mm, depending on drawer size

Length – overall depth of drawer less $\frac{1}{3}$ thickness of drawer front.

*Front:* Width – a tight push fit between the top and bottom drawer rails

Thickness – 14 mm to 20 mm depending on drawer size

Length – a tight push fit.

*Back:* Width – width of sides less about 15 mm

Thickness – same as sides

Length – a tight push fit between vertical drawer rails.

NOTE: *all ends to be shot (planed) dead square*

Step 2 *Setting out and making up*

Follow standard practice for setting out and making through and lap dovetails, with the following exceptions.

(a) Allow no waste at ends of pins and tails – shoulders to be exactly thickness of wood from ends.

(b) There is a special arrangement of pins and tails at the back (Fig. 89).

(c) The top edge of the drawer back is slightly rounded and set down about 3 mm below the top edge of the sides (Fig. 89).

(d) The top of the grooves for the drawer bottom must be exactly level with the bottom edge of the drawer back.

(e) If the sides are to be grooved, they and the front should be grooved before the drawer is assembled. If slips are to be fitted, this should be done after gluing and cleaning up is completed.

(f) Fitting the drawer to the carcase opening is carried out by planing first the sides (Fig. 90) and then the edges, until a smooth sliding fit is obtained.

Step 3 *Drawer bottom*

The drawer bottom may be made from solid timber, but is better made from plywood. It should be made to slide freely along the grooves in the sides or slips, then trimmed to fit squarely into the groove in the drawer front. About 3 mm overhang is left at the back of the drawer. The bottom is held in position at the rear by means of two or three countersunk screws, fitting into slots if there is a solid wood bottom (to allow for any movement), as in Fig. 91, or into ordinary counter-sunk holes if there is a plywood bottom.

## Drawer front, handles and lock

Methods of decorating drawer fronts and the design and fitting of handles and locks are described in Chapters 3 and 4, pages 52–3 and 56–60.

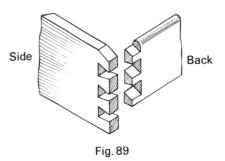

Fig. 89

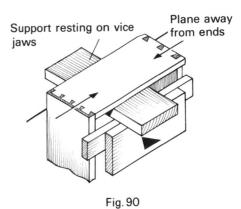

Fig. 90

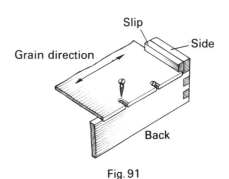

Fig. 91

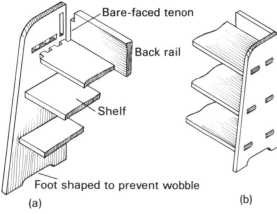

Bare-faced tenon

Back rail

Shelf

Foot shaped to prevent wobble

(a)                (b)

Fig. 92

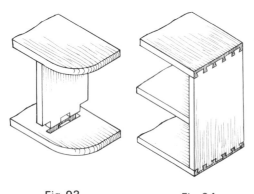

Fig. 93            Fig. 94

**Carcases** (other than boxes and drawers)
Fig. 92 to 96 show different carcase constructions.
Each form has its own peculiarities, but it must be
emphasised that the method of tackling each job
should always follow the procedure already laid
down.

Fig. 92a shows a simple form of carcase suitable
for open bookcases and racks. The shelves are
housed and morticed and tenoned into the ends, the
tenons being stopped if an unbroken outside face is
preferred, or taken right through the thickness of
the end and chamfered to give a decorative effect
(Fig. 92b).

In Fig. 93 the uprights are tenoned into top and
bottom shelves, and the ends are rounded off. A
shelf unit of this kind is often useful in the kitchen
and can be fitted with sliding glass doors if required
(see Chapter 3, pages 48–9).

When a carcase free from projecting shelves or
ends is required, it may be dovetailed or lap
dovetailed together as in Fig. 94. If all joints are to
be hidden, then the more complicated construction
shown in Fig. 95a should be used. The carcase end
may be made in solid wood or framed up as in Fig.
96. In both cases the top, usually 10 mm to 16 mm
thick, is screwed on from the underside of the two
lap-dovetailed rails. The front edge and ends of the
top may be set in from the front edge and ends of
the carcase and moulded or may overhang them as
shown in Fig. 95b.

Notice how the back rail is set forward by the
thickness of the plywood back which is screwed into
a rebate cut in the rear edge of the carcase end.
Other problems connected with the fitting of carcase
backs are shown in Fig. 97 to 101.

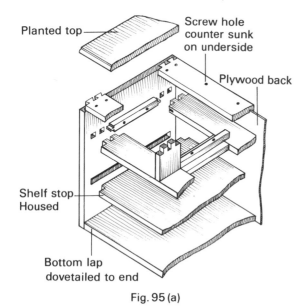

Planted top

Screw hole
counter sunk
on underside

Plywood back

Shelf stop
Housed

Bottom lap
dovetailed to end

Fig. 95 (a)

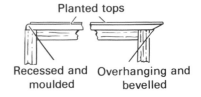

Planted tops

Recessed and       Overhanging and
moulded            bevelled

Fig. 95 (b)

Drawer rails are jointed to the carcase ends and to each other by double (twin) mortice and tenons, drawer runners being fitted between each pair by means of stub (short) tenons (Fig. 95c). If a wide solid wood carcase end is used it is stiffened by means of 'ear pieces' glued to the cross rails (Fig. 95d).

Depending upon the type of carcase construction used, the method of fitting the back will require careful thought. Nowadays, carcase backs are nearly always made of plywood of 3 mm to 8 mm thickness, fitted in one of three ways.

(a) The back can be screwed directly on to the back of the carcase (Fig. 97a). As this is rather unsightly the back should be set in from the edges as in Fig. 97b.

(b) The back can be rebated as in Fig. 98a. The back may be screwed direct to the carcase (Fig. 98b), or held in place by a moulding pinned to the rebate (Fig. 98c). (Screwing the back directly to the carcase strengthens the construction as a whole and is often done when making large cupboards, etc.)

If the back of a through dovetailed carcase is fitted in this way, a 'cogging' piece must be left on the tails piece to fill the space where the rebate is cut along the pins piece (Fig. 98d).

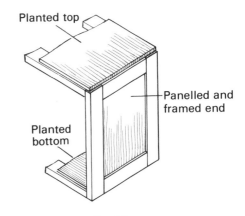

Fig. 96

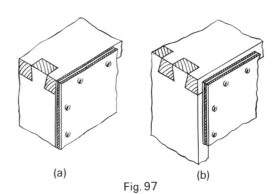

(a)                    (b)

Fig. 97

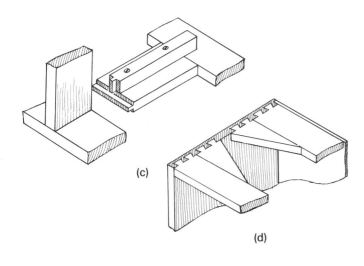

(c)

(d)

Fig. 95

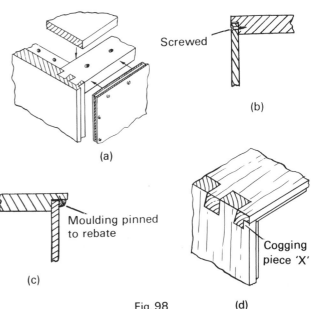

(a)

Screwed

(b)

Moulding pinned to rebate

(c)

Cogging piece 'X'

Fig. 98          (d)

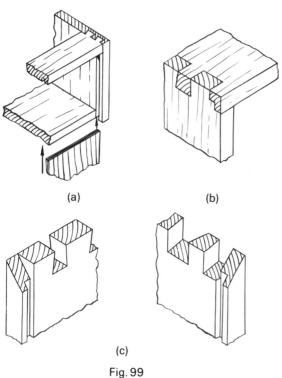

(a)                    (b)

(c)

Fig. 99

(c) The back can be grooved in as in Fig. 99a. The plywood back is slid in from underneath and held in place by a few screws passing through it into the back edge of the carcase bottom.

Again, the through dovetailed carcase provides a problem, but this may be overcome either by using a cogging piece (Fig. 99b) or by mitring the rear corner of the joint as in Fig. 99c.

This may be matched by mitring the front corners of a through dovetailed carcase which gives a very neat appearance (Fig. 100).

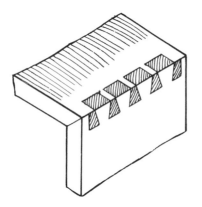

Fig. 100

# 3 Miscellaneous Processes, Fittings and Adhesives

## SHAPING

### Simple shaping

Shaping wood for the end of a book rack, a circular table top, or the hole for a loudspeaker in a radio cabinet, for example, is done in three main stages.

NOTE: *shaping normally follows cutting of joints, as marking out of joints is often difficult or impossible afterwards.*

Stage 1 *Marking out*

If the shape is geometrical (Fig. 101a), it may be drawn out directly on the wood with a ruler, pencil and compasses. If a more complex curve is required (Fig. 101b), first prepare a template.

The template may be cut out of thick paper and stuck on to the work (Fig. 102a), or the shape may be drawn on to the wood by pencilling round a card template (Fig. 102b).

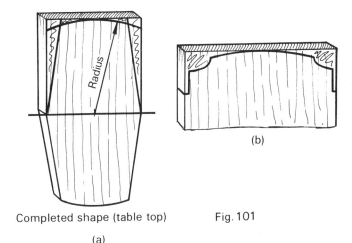

Completed shape (table top)　　　Fig. 101

(a)

(b)

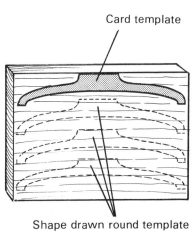

Paper template (pattern) glued to wood

Card template

Shape drawn round template

(a)　　　　　　　　　　(b)

Fig. 102

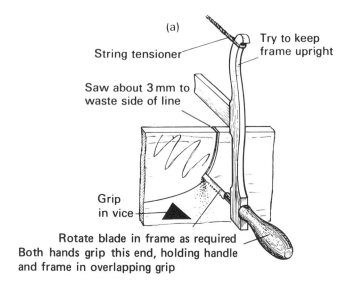

(a)

String tensioner

Try to keep frame upright

Saw about 3 mm to waste side of line

Grip in vice

Rotate blade in frame as required
Both hands grip this end, holding handle and frame in overlapping grip

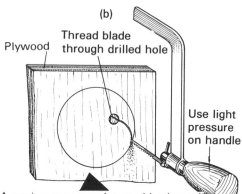

(b)

Plywood

Thread blade through drilled hole

Use light pressure on handle

*NOTE:* A coping saw may be used horizontally as shown, with teeth facing forward; or vertically (handle underneath) with teeth facing towards handle, cutting on the down stroke.

Fig. 103

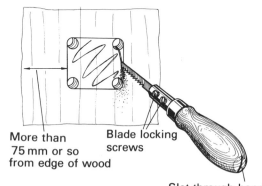

More than 75 mm or so from edge of wood

Blade locking screws

Slot through handle for retracting blade

Fig. 104

**Stage 2** *Cutting (sawing)*

Most of the waste may be removed with a saw. A tenon saw or fine toothed cross-cut saw is used for cutting straight lines, and a bow or coping saw for curved shapes. The coping saw is used for thin material and the stronger bladed bow saw for thicker timber (Fig. 103a and b). For very fine work, a fretsaw (Fig. 279) may be used.

If a shaped hole has to be cut more than about 75 mm from the edge of a panel, a pad saw or compass saw will be used (Fig. 104, 280 and 281). When cutting a hole, first drill a small hole so that the blade of the saw can be inserted. Notice, too, how rounded corners can be bored out.

**Stage 3** *Trueing up*

The waste left after sawing can be removed by using the methods shown in Fig. 105 to 110. Curves of small radius are usually trued up by paring (Fig. 105 to 107). Larger curves are smoothed with a spokeshave. For convex (outside) curves use the flat-soled spokeshave (Fig. 108), but for concave (inside) curves use a spokeshave with a rounded sole (Fig. 109).

As in planing, care must be taken to work only 'with the grain' (Fig. 110). For rough shaping of softwoods a 'Surform' type of file (Fig. 338) may be used.

Final smoothing (before polishing or painting) is carried out by glasspapering, using medium glasspaper followed by fine grade (see also Chapter 7). The most economical way to use standard-sized sheets of glasspaper (280 mm × 230 mm) is to cut them into six smaller pieces. These will then fit conveniently over a cork 'rubber' or block which should always be used to ensure that an even surface is obtained (Fig. 111). Shaped wooden blocks are used when glasspapering mouldings (Fig. 112).

## Laminating

Laminating simply means sticking together thin sheets or strips of wood. In plywood, each 'ply' or veneer is positioned with its grain running at right angles to the veneers glued to either side of it. This gives it considerable strength and stability. A curved shape built up from thin strips (laminations) has greater strength than one shaped from solid wood, and any tendency to split owing to 'short grain' is overcome (Fig. 113a and b). A stacking chair (Fig. 114) made entirely from laminations is not only strong but also very light, and its one-piece seat and back give a certain amount of 'spring'.

Fig. 108

Fig. 109

Fig. 110

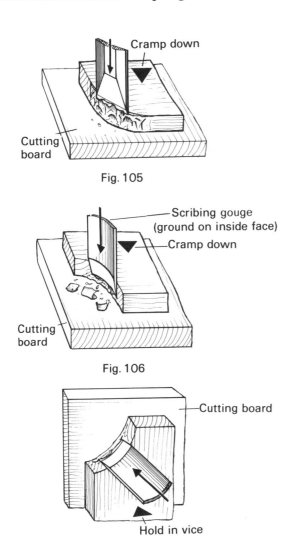

Cramp down

Cutting board

Fig. 105

Scribing gouge (ground on inside face)

Cramp down

Cutting board

Fig. 106

Cutting board

Hold in vice

Fig. 107

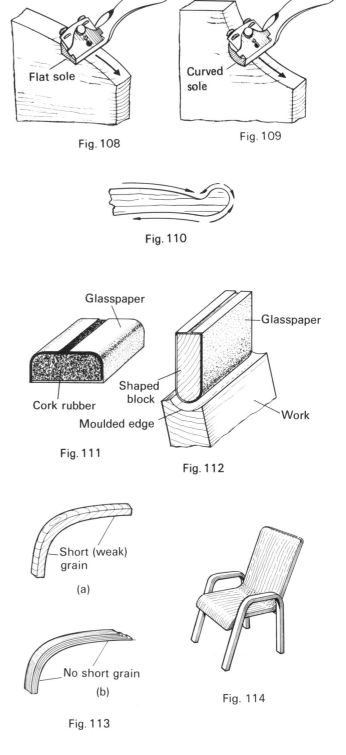

Glasspaper

Glasspaper

Cork rubber

Shaped block

Moulded edge

Work

Fig. 111

Fig. 112

Short (weak) grain

(a)

No short grain

(b)

Fig. 113

Fig. 114

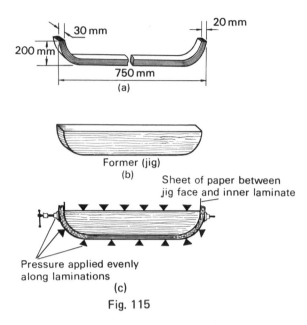

Former (jig)
(b)

Sheet of paper between
jig face and inner laminate

Pressure applied evenly
along laminations
(c)

Fig. 115

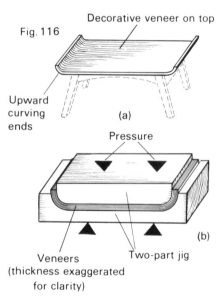

Fig. 116

Decorative veneer on top

Upward
curving
ends

(a)

Pressure

Veneers
(thickness exaggerated
for clarity)

Two-part jig

(b)

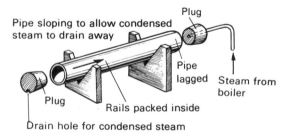

Pipe sloping to allow condensed
steam to drain away

Plug

Pipe
lagged

Steam from
boiler

Plug

Rails packed inside

Drain hole for condensed steam

Fig. 117

The laminated sledge runner shown in Fig. 115a would be made as follows:

Step 1 Prepare five strips of straight-grained ash about 1·2 m long (or rather longer than the total length of runner required) × 30 mm × 4 mm. If the strips are accurately machine-sawn they will not require planing.

Step 2 Make a former or jig by cutting the exact shape of the inside of the curve on the edge of a stout board (Fig. 115b).

Step 3 Apply a synthetic resin adhesive to the sides of the strips (laminations) and assemble them as shown in Fig. 115c, applying pressure evenly along the whole length of the runner by means of G cramps, short sash cramps, or by any other method which is available. Put a sheet of thick paper between the jig and the first lamination to prevent it from sticking to the face of the jig.

Step 4 When the adhesive is completely set, the runner may be cleaned up in the usual way.

The shaped coffee table top shown in Fig. 116a could be made in much the same way, but here it would be advisable to use a two-part jig (Fig. 116b) to enable pressure to be applied evenly over the whole surface of the top.

**Steam Bending**

This is an alternative to laminating, which is very useful (a) when fairly narrow rails are required, and/or (b) when only a limited number of such curved parts are needed.

In this process, the fibres of suitable timber are softened by steaming (literally by cooking them) so that the wood becomes pliable. It is then cramped to a former as in Fig. 115c, and left until the moisture has dried out. After this it will retain its new shape.

Not all timbers are suited to this treatment; among the best are beech and ash.

A simple steaming device can be made from a length of 100 mm to 150 mm cast iron, steel or asbestos pipe, suitably lagged to help retain the heat. Wooden plugs are fitted to each end; one is connected to a small boiler for producing the steam, and the other has a small outlet hole in it. Fig. 117 shows such a steamer in diagrammatic form.

The rails are packed loosely inside the tube, end plugs replaced, and steam passed through for a period of half an hour to four hours depending upon the thickness of the rails.

NOTE:

(a) *Great care must be taken to ensure that the apparatus is not touched when in use, as the steam or hot pipe can cause severe scalds or burns.*

(b) *Loosely tying the strips together before putting them into the steamer will simplify their removal while still hot.*

(c) *It is essential to wear thick gloves when handling the freshly steamed timber, which should be cramped to a former (jig) before it cools down.*

For softening strips of wood up to about one metre in length, immersion in a tank of gently boiling water is often employed. Fig. 118 shows such a simple arrangement. This method is generally used when thicker lengths of wood have to be bent as it is more powerful in its softening action than steaming.

## WEDGING

Wedges serve two useful purposes in woodworking: they are (a) a means of holding or cramping work together, and (b) a means of locking joints, such as the mortice and tenon, very firmly.

To illustrate (a), using the example in Fig. 115c, wedges can be used instead of cramps (see Fig. 119). Fig. 120 shows a similar use of wedges for tightly cramping boards together when nailing them to a batten. Only one set of wedges is shown; this arrangement would be repeated at the other end of the boards.

To illustrate (b), through mortice and tenon joints may be wedged as in Fig. 121a and b. This reinforcement and locking of the tenon in the mortice is often carried out in joinery work such as the making of gates, doors, and window frames.

Fig. 121a shows wedges driven in at the ends of the mortice, but Fig. 121b shows a much better method, in which the wedges cause the end parts of the tenon to be splayed out in dovetail fashion thus holding it firmly in place. In this case, the outer end of the mortice is made a little wider (about 2 mm) than the inner end, to allow for the splaying of the tenon.

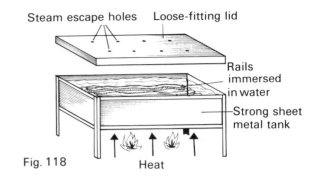

Steam escape holes   Loose-fitting lid

Rails immersed in water

Strong sheet metal tank

Fig. 118          Heat

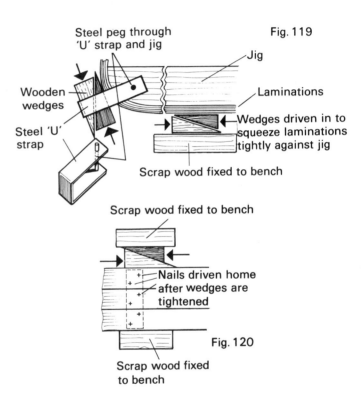

Fig. 119

Steel peg through 'U' strap and jig

Jig

Wooden wedges

Laminations

Steel 'U' strap

Wedges driven in to squeeze laminations tightly against jig

Scrap wood fixed to bench

Scrap wood fixed to bench

Nails driven home after wedges are tightened

Fig. 120

Scrap wood fixed to bench

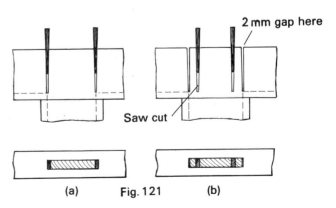

2 mm gap here

Saw cut

(a)     Fig. 121     (b)

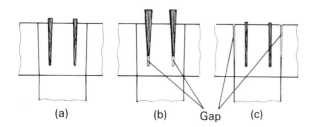

(a)          (b)    Gap    (c)

Fig. 122

Wedges are cut from straight grained timber and are usually about 4 mm thick at the wider end, tapering to the thin end which just fits into the saw cut made in the tenon. When hammered in, the wedge should fill the slot completely (Fig. 122a). Fig. 122b and c show the result of using wedges having too much or too little taper.

Wedges may also be used for their decorative effect (see Chapter 4).

## FITTING TABLE TOPS

When a solid wooden top is to be fitted to a table or stool frame, allowance has to be made for expansion and contraction across the grain. Moreover, it is preferable to fix the top from underneath, so that no screws, nail-holes, or plugs show on the top surface.

Fig. 123a to d shows different methods of fixing table tops which take account of both these points.

*Buttoning* (Fig. 123a) – wooden buttons fitting into mortices or grooves worked on the inside of the top rails allow for expansion and contraction of the top (this is the traditional method).

*Pocket screwing* (Fig. 123b) and *Counter boring* (Fig. 123c) – as these methods do not really allow for 'movement', they are best used for fixing block-board, plywood, or chipboard tops.

*Slotted metal* (Fig. 123d) – screws passing through the slots into the table top slide along the grooves if any movement takes place.

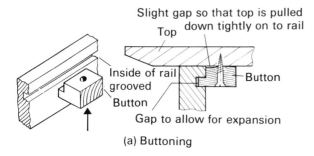

(a) Buttoning

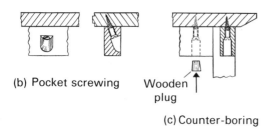

(b) Pocket screwing        Wooden
plug

(c) Counter-boring

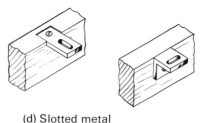

(d) Slotted metal

Fig. 123

## SIMPLE UPHOLSTERY AND WOVEN TOPS FOR CHAIRS AND STOOLS

Two simple ways of upholstering a dining seat or stool top are shown in Fig. 124a and 125a; and two patterns for weaving seagrass or cord tops are shown in Fig. 126a and 127a.

**Loose or drop-in seat** (Fig. 124a)
This is a padded frame which fits into a rebate cut in the top rails of the stool or chair (Fig. 124b). It can be completed in seven stages.

Step 1 Make the frame from 42 mm × 18 mm section birch or similar hardwood, jointing the corners with bridle or dowelled butt joints. The frame should fit into the rebates with about 3 mm clearance all round (Fig. 124b) to allow for the thickness of covering materials. The top outer edges should be chamfered to 'soften' the edges of the padding.

Step 2 Tack 40 mm wide woven webbing (or rubberised canvas webbing, which is much better, as it is springy) tightly across the frame, interweaving the strips for extra strength. Three strips fixed in each direction are usually enough.

Step 3 Place hessian (clean sacking) over the webbing and tack to the top of the frame.

Step 4 Stick a slightly oversized sheet of rubber latex or plastic foam (about 40 mm thick) to the hessian with blobs of contact adhesive at intervals to hold it in place.

Step 5 Spread a second piece of hessian over the foam and tack off to the underneath of the frame. This hessian should be stretched fairly tightly when tacking off so as to pull the edges of the foam into a rounded shape (Fig. 124c).

Avoid wrinkles by first tacking the centre of each edge of the hessian, then working towards the corners (Fig. 124d), 'stroking' the hessian towards the corner being tacked. Cut away any surplus hessian at the corners to avoid bulky lumps.

Step 6 Now tack the covering material (fabric or plastics coated cloth) in the same way, but do not strain as tightly as the hessian or it will pucker.

Step 7 Trim away any surplus material from under the frame.

NOTE: *use tacks about 15 mm long for the webbing and rather shorter ones for the remainder of the job.*

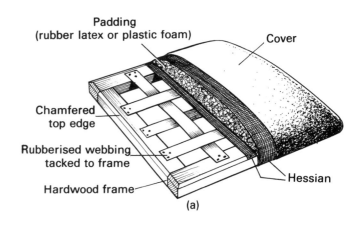

Padding (rubber latex or plastic foam) — Cover — Chamfered top edge — Rubberised webbing tacked to frame — Hardwood frame — Hessian

(a)

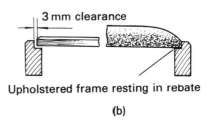

3 mm clearance

Upholstered frame resting in rebate

(b)

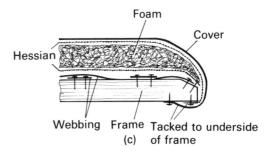

Foam — Cover — Hessian — Webbing — Frame — Tacked to underside of frame

(c)

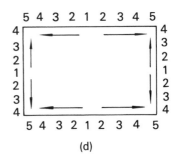

(d)

Fig. 124

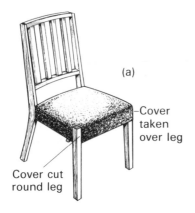

Cover taken over leg

Cover cut round leg

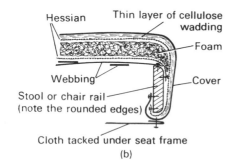

Hessian

Thin layer of cellulose wadding

Foam

Webbing

Stool or chair rail (note the rounded edges)

Cover

Cloth tacked under seat frame

(b)

Fig. 125

### Stuff-over upholstered seat

In place of a loose seat it may be preferable to pad the actual stool or chair frame rails as in Fig. 125a, the covering materials being taken right over the top rails.

Fig. 125b shows the method, which is basically similar to that used for padding the loose frame. Differences are: (a) the webbing and first layer of hessian are tacked to the top edge of the seat rail, but the other layers are taken round the rail before being tacked off; and (b) a layer of cellulose wadding (rather like cheap cotton wool) is placed under the top cover to 'soften' the rails.

### Woven tops in seagrass or cord

Two woven patterns easily produced are 'squares' (Fig. 126a) and mitre patterns (Fig. 127a).

### 'Square' pattern

Step 1 Wind the seagrass or cord into a conveniently-sized ball, tack the end to the inside of the rail, and take the seagrass across and round the top rails as in Fig. 126b. (Be careful to wind it quite slackly as it will tighten up later.)

The number of turns wound on must divide exactly by the number of cords which appear in each square of the pattern (usually 5 or 6 cords – see Fig. 126d). Any joins in the cord should be tied underneath.

Step 2 Using a thin strip of wood about 20 mm × 6 mm, weave it through the turns of cord as in Fig. 126d, keeping alternately 5 (6) turns over and 5 (6) turns under the strip.

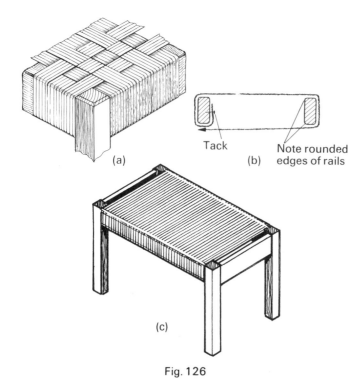

Tack

Note rounded edges of rails

(a)

(b)

(c)

Fig. 126

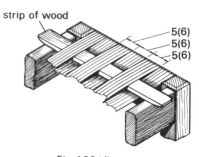

strip of wood

5(6)
5(6)
5(6)

Fig. 126 (d)

Step 3 Thread the cord 5 (6) turns through the 'tunnel' formed by the wooden strip, pulling each turn as tight as possible.

Step 4 Remove the strip and re-insert it 'over' and 'under' where it was previously 'under' and 'over', and weave another 5 (6) turns of the cord.

Step 5 Repeat steps (2), (3) and (4) until the whole width of the top has been woven, tying off the loose end of the cord underneath.

NOTE: *a length of 3 mm diameter wire, with a hooked end through which the cord is threaded, is useful for feeding the cord through the 'tunnel' made by the wooden strip.*

## Mitred pattern

This pattern (Fig. 127a) is built up by winding the cord in a continuous 'under, over and round' action as shown in Fig. 127b.

The cord or seagrass should be kept pulled tight and the 'mitres' kept even as the work proceeds.

If the seat is rectangular rather than square in plan, the end rails will be 'filled' before the longer sides (Fig. 127c). In this case finish the weaving by going from side to side following a figure of eight course as shown in Fig. 127d. Fig. 127e shows the completed pattern.

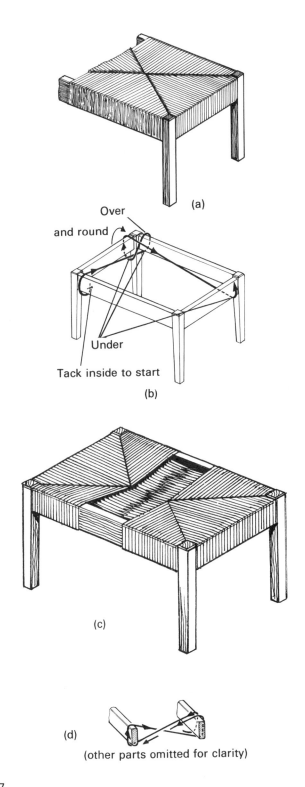

(a)

Over
and round
Under
Tack inside to start
(b)

(c)

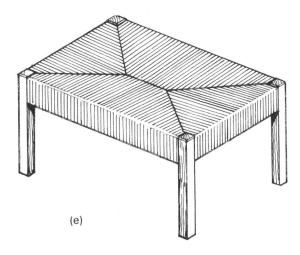

(e)

(d)

(other parts omitted for clarity)

Fig. 127

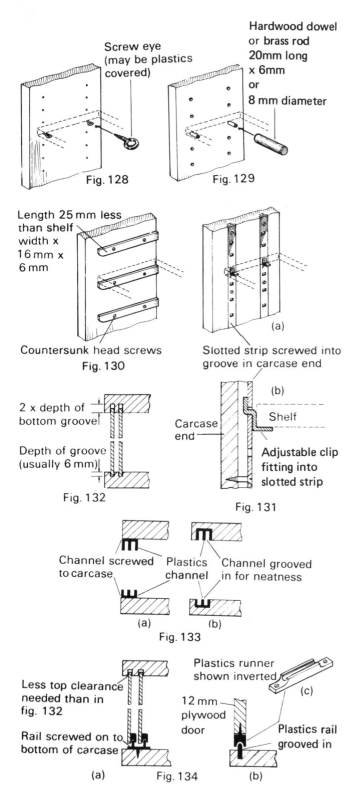

Screw eye (may be plastics covered)

**Fig. 128**

Hardwood dowel or brass rod 20mm long x 6mm or 8 mm diameter

**Fig. 129**

Length 25 mm less than shelf width x 16 mm x 6 mm

Countersunk head screws

**Fig. 130**

Slotted strip screwed into groove in carcase end

(a)

(b)

Carcase end

Shelf

Adjustable clip fitting into slotted strip

**Fig. 131**

2 x depth of bottom groove

Depth of groove (usually 6 mm)

**Fig. 132**

Channel screwed to carcase

Plastics channel

Channel grooved in for neatness

(a)        (b)

**Fig. 133**

Less top clearance needed than in fig. 132

Rail screwed on to bottom of carcase

Plastics runner shown inverted

(c)

12 mm plywood door

Plastics rail grooved in

(a)        **Fig. 134**        (b)

## ADJUSTABLE SHELVES

Shelves fitted to bookcases, china cabinets and many other types of cupboard are often more useful if they are adjustable for height.

Figs. 128 to 131 show methods of fitting adjustable shelves to carcases such as those illustrated in Figs. 94, 95a, and 96.

Remember that if the shelves are loose and not jointed to the carcase ends, more strain is put on to the carcase corner joints, which must be strong and well fitting. A screwed-on plywood back (Fig. 98b) will also give extra rigidity to the carcase.

Shelves made from 6 mm thick glass may also be supported by the methods shown in Figs. 128 to 131.

Screw eyes and dowels (Figs. 128 and 129) are very simple ways of supporting shelves, pairs of holes of suitable diameter being drilled at about 25 mm vertical spacing. If the shelf positions are to be adjusted very often, some wear in the holes will take place and the dowels or screw eyes may become rather too loose-fitting for safety.

Screwed-on strips of thin section hardwood may be used (Fig. 130), but a disadvantage is that they may appear rather unsightly.

Fig. 131a shows commercially-manufactured slotted strips which are screwed into shallow grooves ploughed into the carcase ends. Small clips hook into these slots and support the shelf ends (Fig. 131b). This method of shelf adjustment is often used in libraries – it is neat in appearance and effective in use.

## SLIDING DOORS

It is sometimes convenient to have sliding rather than hinged doors, using unframed plate glass, plywood, or plastic-surfaced hardboard.

For doors of up to 600 mm × 600 mm, the methods shown in Figs. 132 to 134 are suitable. Where top and bottom chanelling is used, either plastic or ploughed from the solid wood, the top groove must be at least twice as deep as the bottom groove, as the door is put in by lifting it into the top groove and then dropping it into the bottom one.

For larger doors, special sliding door gear is obtainable, fitted with rollers instead of simple runners to give an easier opening and closing action by reducing friction.

## FITTING AND HINGING DOORS

### Fitting

Framed up doors (see Chapter 2) are usually hinged to fit inside the carcase (Fig. 135). As the door will have been made 1 mm to 2 mm oversize, it should be 'fitted' to the carcase in four stages.

Step 1 Plane the edge of the hinging stile.

Step 2 Plane the top edge so that it and the hinging stile fit neatly against the inside of the carcase.

Step 3 Plane the bottom edge so that when the door is tight against (1) and (2) in Fig. 135, there is at least 1 mm clearance all along (3).

Step 4 Plane the edge of the locking stile (4 in Fig. 135) to give a small amount of clearance. Further slight adjustment may be necessary after hinging.

### Hinging

Hinging calls for great accuracy in setting out and cutting. Butt hinges (Fig. 143a) may be fitted with the thickness of the knuckle set wholly into the door (Fig. 136a), as is usual in cabinet work, or half into the door and half into the carcase (Fig. 136b). Heavy doors (house doors) are hinged in this way. In the case of Fig. 136a, the rear part of the carcase leaf is housed into the carcase (Fig. 137).

Because it is extremely difficult to hinge a door to be quite flush all round the carcase edge, it is usual to inset the door very slightly, to 'break' the line, as in Fig. 137.

Step 1 Assuming the door is to be hinged as in Fig. 136a (full thickness of knuckle into door stile), it should be marked out as in Fig. 138a. Fig. 138b, c, and d show the gauge settings are obtained.

If the hinge is to be set in as in Fig. 136b, half of the knuckle thickness should be set on the gauge as in Fig. 138e and marked on both door and carcase edges.

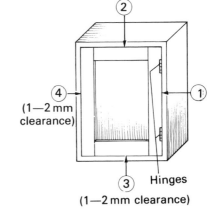

Fig. 135

(1—2 mm clearance)
(1—2 mm clearance)
Hinges

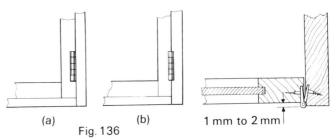

(a)    (b)    1 mm to 2 mm

Fig. 136
Fig. 137

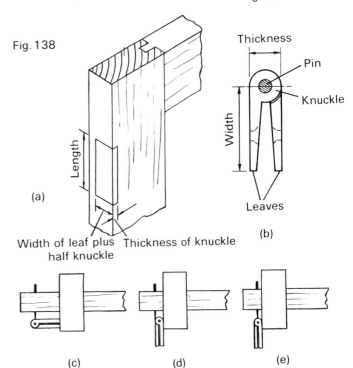

Fig. 138

Thickness
Pin
Knuckle
Width
Length
Leaves

(a)
(b)

Width of leaf plus half knuckle    Thickness of knuckle

(c)    (d)    (e)

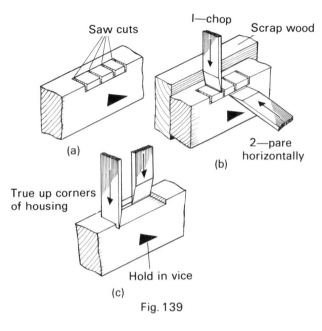

True up corners of housing

Hold in vice

(c)

Fig. 139

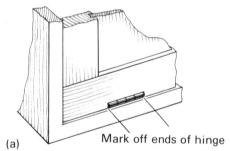

Mark off ends of hinge

(a)

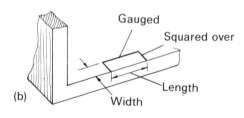

Gauged

Squared over

Length

Width

(b)

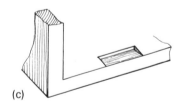

(c)

Fig. 140

The hinge is set at least its own length in from the top and bottom edges of the door to avoid screwing into the end grain of the tenons.

Step 2 Cut away the waste wood for the hinge housing as in Fig. 139a to c and screw in the hinge.

Step 3 Mark off the hinge position on to the edge of the carcase (Fig. 140a), square the length, and gauge the width of the hinge as in Fig. 140b.

Cut a sloping housing as in Fig. 140c, offer up the hinged door to the carcase (that is, position the door accurately), and screw the hinge leaf into it.

Step 4 After hinging, the rear edge of the locking stile may catch on the carcase as the door shuts (Fig. 140d). To prevent this, it should be bevelled slightly as in Fig. 140e.

There are two common faults to watch:

(a) If the hinge has been set in too deeply the door will not close (Fig. 141a); and

(b) if the countersunk screw heads are not set in quite flush with the surface of the hinge leaves, they will touch and prevent the door from closing completely.

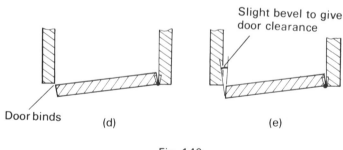

Door binds

(d)

Slight bevel to give door clearance

(e)

Fig. 140

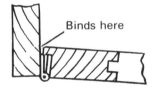

Binds here

(a)

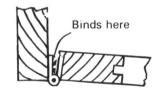

Binds here

Fig. 141

(b)

Butt hinges for heavy doors are usually made of mild steel or cast iron, but for better-class joinery and cabinet work, brass hinges are used (Fig. 143a). Brass butts may be of two kinds: (a) 'solid drawn' (Fig. 142a), made from thick cross section metal, the hole for the pin being drilled from the solid brass – these are expensive but good; or (b) 'folded' (Fig. 142b), cheaper inferior hinges made from sheet brass, the knuckle being formed by bending the metal round the pin.

Other common types of hinges are: (c) back flap (Fig. 143b), with wider leaves so that the screws can be inserted further from the edge of the carcase, used for hinging bureau 'falls', and so on; and (d) tee hinges (Fig. 143c), usually made of mild steel, used for hinging gates and battened and boarded (coal-house type) doors.

## CATCHES

Fig. 144a to g shows examples of different types of door catch, (a) to (d) being fitted into or on to the back of the door, (e) to (g) being fitted to the front of the door.

The ball catch (Fig. 144a and b) is commonly fitted to cupboard doors. The barrel (containing a spring loaded steel ball) fits into a hole drilled into the edge of the door stile. The end plate (fitted to the larger sizes) is then cut into the stile and the catch screwed in position as in Fig. 145a and b.

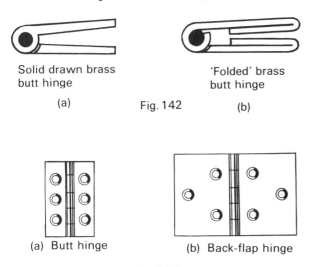

Solid drawn brass butt hinge
(a)

'Folded' brass butt hinge
(b)

Fig. 142

(a) Butt hinge

(b) Back-flap hinge

Fig. 143

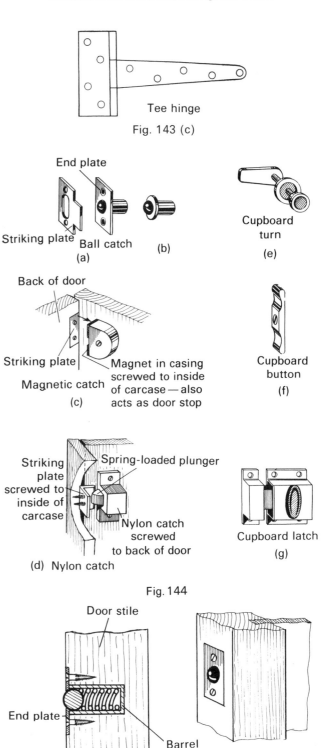

Tee hinge

Fig. 143 (c)

End plate

Striking plate    Ball catch    (b)
(a)

Cupboard turn
(e)

Back of door

Striking plate    Magnet in casing screwed to inside of carcase — also acts as door stop

Magnetic catch
(c)

Cupboard button
(f)

Striking plate screwed to inside of carcase    Spring-loaded plunger

Nylon catch screwed to back of door

(d) Nylon catch

Cupboard latch
(g)

Fig. 144

Door stile

End plate

Barrel

(a)    (b)

Fig. 145

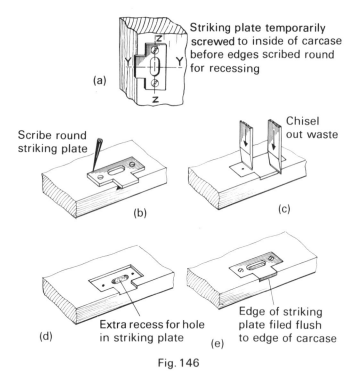

Striking plate temporarily screwed to inside of carcase before edges scribed round for recessing

Scribe round striking plate

Chisel out waste

Extra recess for hole in striking plate

Edge of striking plate filed flush to edge of carcase

Fig. 146

To position the striking plate, close the door a few times. The ball will mark a line on the inside of the carcase to give the centre line Y–Y in Fig. 146a. The vertical centre line Z–Z is half the door thickness in from the front edge of the carcase plus the amount the door itself is inset into the carcase, usually about 1 mm (see Fig. 137). Fig. 146b to e shows how the striking plate is fitted.

## LOCKS

Three popular types of lock are shown in Fig. 147a to c.

**The cut cupboard lock** is fitted from the back of the door as follows:

Step 1 Measure the distance from the pin P to the outside face of the plate O (Fig. 147a), and mark this on to the stile. Drill the hole right through the stile and chisel out the keyhole (Fig. 148a).

Step 2 Scribe and gauge the recess for the body of the lock in its correct position on the stile, and cut out (Fig. 148b).

Step 3 Place the lock in position and scribe the outline of the back plate on to the stile.

Step 4 Chisel out the recess for the back plate and adjust this recess until both back and side (S in Fig. 148c) of the back plate fit flush into the stile. The completed recess is shown in Fig. 148d.

NOTE: *if an escutcheon (Fig. 149a or b) is to be fitted, do this before screwing the lock into place.*

Step 5 On the inside face of the carcase cut a suitable hole for the bolt and fit a striking plate if required.

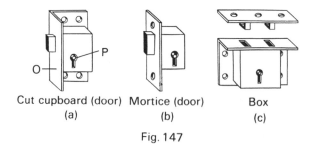

Cut cupboard (door)
(a)

Mortice (door)
(b)

Box
(c)

Fig. 147

**The mortice lock** (Fig. 147b) is fitted similarly to the ball catch.

Step 1 Fit the mechanism into a mortice chopped in the edge of the stile.

Step 2 Scribe the face plate outline on to the door and cut the recess.

Step 3 Find the keyhole position, cut out the keyhole, and fit the escutcheon.

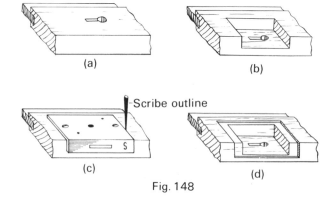

(a)

(b)

Scribe outline

(c)

(d)

Fig. 148

Step 4 Fit the striking plate to the carcase or door jamb as described under instructions for fitting a ball catch (see page 51).

**The box lock** (Fig. 147c) is fitted similarly to the cut cupboard lock.

## HANDLES AND KNOBS

Fig. 150a to k shows a variety of wooden handles and knobs which can easily be made in the workshop. They should be made of close-grained hardwoods and may be fitted by any of the methods shown in Fig. 151a to d.

## ADHESIVES

Adhesives (glues) have been greatly improved during recent years. Modern adhesives are more convenient to use than the traditional animal glue and, because they are applied cold, longer assembly times are permissible. Most of them are damp resistant, and the synthetic resins are completely waterproof. But animal glue is still widely used because of its cheapness; while it is not very convenient to heat animal glue at home for occasional use, this is no problem in a workshop where glue is in constant demand. The table on pages 54–5 compares the different types of adhesive.

NOTE: *not all the precautions needed with animal or other glues can be shown in the table.*

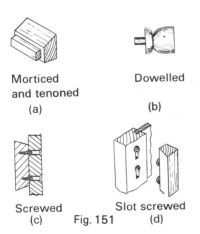

Morticed and tenoned
(a)

Dowelled
(b)

Screwed
(c)        Fig. 151        Slot screwed
(d)

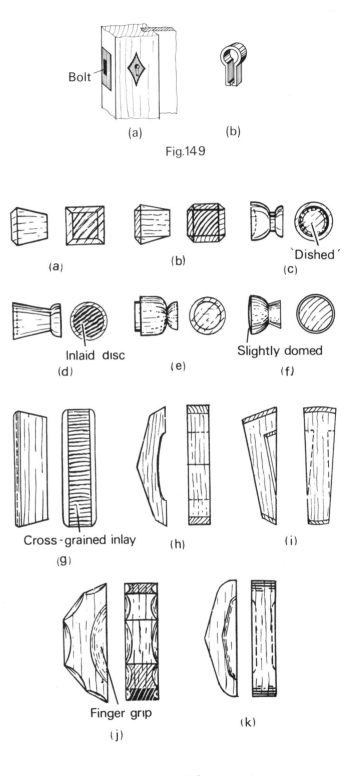

Bolt
(a)                    (b)
Fig. 149

(a)                    (b)                    'Dished'
(c)

Inlaid disc
(d)                    (e)                    Slightly domed
(f)

Cross-grained inlay
(g)                    (h)                    (i)

Finger grip
(j)                    (k)

Fig. 150

If the insides of carcases, stool legs and stretcher rails, etc., are polished before gluing, surplus glue which cannot stick to polished surfaces can be easily removed with a damp rag (the exception is contact adhesive which needs a special solvent). Remember to scrape polish off any tenons, dovetails, or other parts where the glue is to grip.

**Animal glue** must be kept quite dry during storage. Damp will cause it to putrify (go mouldy). The glue container should be of aluminium or 'tinned' iron; iron will contaminate the glue, causing it to become a dirty brown colour. Thoroughly scald out the container before use to get rid of old putrified glue.

Heat the glue in a water-jacketed container (Fig. 152) but do NOT boil. This seriously reduces the glue's strength. Good quality Scotch glue is brittle, translucent and of a light amber colour. Dark rubbery glue should be replaced. Animal glue may be bought in powdered, granular (pearl) or cake (Scotch) forms.

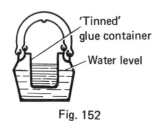

'Tinned' glue container

Water level

Fig. 152

## ADHESIVES

| TYPE | SOURCE | PREPARATION FOR USE | APPLICATION |
|---|---|---|---|
| **Animal glue** (Scotch, bone or hide) | extracted from cleaned bones or hides by steaming under pressure | soak in water and heat to 60°C in water jacketed container | apply quickly in warm room to both parts of the joint |
| **Casein** | skimmed milk treated with formaldehyde; the curds produced dried and ground into powder | powder is mixed with measured quantity of water. Stir well | apply to both parts of the joint |
| **Synthetic resin** | made from urea and formaldehyde 'hardener' is strongly acidic | powder is mixed with measured quantity of water (see additional note) | 'One part' type: apply to both parts of joint 'Two part' type: apply resin to one part of joint, acid hardener to other part |
| **PVA** | Polyvinyl acetate | Sold ready mixed (creamy consistency) | apply to both parts of the joint; thickens if temperature is too low |
| **Contact (impact)** | Rubber-based | sold ready mixed (sticky syrup) | apply to both surfaces and allow to dry before bringing surfaces together |

**Synthetic resin adhesives** consist of (a) a synthetic resin, and (b) an acid hardener which quickens the chemical 'curing' (setting) of the resin.

The resin and hardener may be either (a) separate (as in 'Aerolite 306'), resin being applied to one half of the joint and hardener to the other, or (b) combined in powder form (as in 'Cascamite Waterproof') and prepared by mixing with water.

In all cases the manufacturers' instructions should be closely followed.

**Contact (impact) adhesives** are different from other adhesives because the two glued surfaces bond instantly they are brought into contact. For this reason it is impossible to slide one surface over the other to make any adjustments. They must, therefore, be *exactly* positioned in relation to each other before being pressed together.

## ADHESIVES (continued)

| SETTING TIME | RESISTANCE TO DAMP | ECONOMY | REMARKS |
|---|---|---|---|
| 'gels' rapidly, but sets by water drying out. Leave in cramps overnight | none – for internal use only | cheap; unused glue may be reheated for future use (see additional note) | traditional cabinet maker's glue – specially useful for certain veneered work |
| leave in cramps overnight | damp resistant only | mixed glue not used within 24 hours of mixing will be wasted | liable to stain hardwoods – commonly used for interior softwood joinery |
| leave in cramps overnight unless setting temperature is high | completely waterproof – use for external woodwork, boat building, etc. | mixed 'one part' glue not used at the time will be wasted. Resin syrup used with separate acid hardener has shelf life of several weeks ('two part' type is therefore more economical) | some acid hardeners may stain certain hardwoods; wash hands after use and avoid acid splashes |
| leave in cramps for several hours | very little – for internal use only | store in glass or plastics container and keep lid tightly sealed. Shelf life 1–2 years. Fairly expensive | very clean and convenient to use – does not stain; much used for furniture making |
| takes about 15 minutes to dry, joint surfaces bond (set) immediately on contact | damp proof | expensive – keep lid tightly sealed or adhesive will set in the tin | used for fixing laminated plastics, etc., to plywood (see additional note) |

# 4 Decorative Processes

The appearance of many pieces of woodwork may be considerably improved by decorating them, but decoration should never be added to a job as an afterthought. It MUST be thought of as part of the original design (see Chapter 11).

The types of decoration (other than finishes) usually applied to woodwork are (a) veneering and inlaying; (b) decorative use of joints; (c) shaping, chamfers and mouldings; (d) surface tooling and gougework leading to carving, either 'bas relief' or 'in the round' (carving and treenwork are described in Chapter 5).

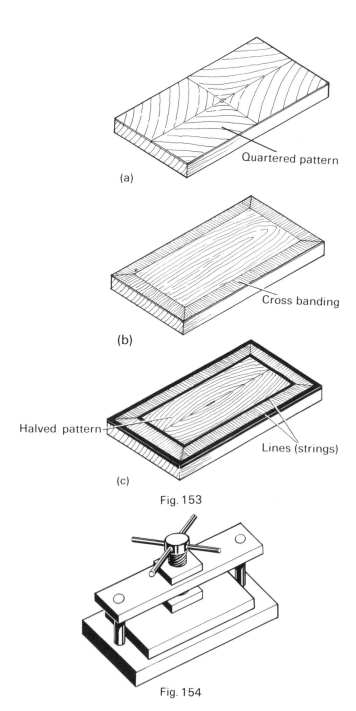

(a)

Quartered pattern

(b)

Cross banding

(c)

Halved pattern

Lines (strings)

Fig. 153

Fig. 154

## VENEERING AND INLAYING

Veneering is in its simplest form the gluing of a thin sheet of decoratively grained wood on to a piece of plain grained timber. Very attractive patterns may be produced by laying the veneers as shown in Fig. 153a and b. Fig. 153c shows the addition to the pattern of *lines* (thin strips of wood). Methods of producing veneers and the fixing of plastic laminates are described in Chapter 8.

There are two basic methods of applying veneers:

*A veneer press* (Fig. 154) must be used if
(a) synthetic resin or PVA glue is employed;
(b) the veneer pattern consists of a number of small pieces (as in marquetry); or
(c) the 'ground' (the wood being veneered) is curved – here a *caul* (Fig. 159) is needed.

*A veneer hammer* (Fig. 155) may be used for veneering flat surfaces when animal glue is employed.

In all cases the ground and the veneers must first be prepared.

### Preparation of the ground

For both methods, the piece of wood to be veneered should be flat and free from cracks or other defects. Knots should be cut out and carefully plugged.

Where the ground is unsupported, as in a flush cupboard door, it should be veneered on both sides to prevent warping as the veneer dries out.

The face(s) should be roughened with a toothing plane (Fig. 308) fitted with a special blade having a serrated edge (Fig. 156). This ensures a good 'key' for the glue. If a toothing plane is not available, a piece of hacksaw blade may be used instead.

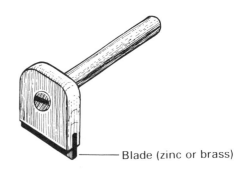

Blade (zinc or brass)

Fig. 155

## Preparation and cutting to size of veneers

If the veneer is overdry and brittle, or if it is badly crinkled, it should be wetted on both sides and flattened by lightly pressing between two flat blocks of wood. After a few hours the veneer may be cut to size without danger of splitting. Veneers are cut about 6 mm oversize to allow for trimming after laying. Cut and trim with a very sharp chisel or keen edged knife, using a straight edge as a guide and supporting the veneer on a smooth sheet of plywood (Fig. 157). Try to cut through the veneer with one steady stroke. The straight edge may be clamped down if the veneer is a large one.

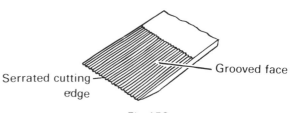

Serrated cutting edge

Grooved face

Fig. 156

## The press method

Prepare as described above.

Step 1 *Laying*

Apply synthetic resin glue to the underside of the dampened veneer(s) and the face(s) of the ground, and place in position in the press. To prevent the adhesive sticking to the faces of the press, place thick sheets of paper or polythene between them and the veneer(s) (Fig. 158).

Step 2 When the adhesive has set, remove the work from the press and trim away the surplus veneer.

Step 3 Scrape the outer face of the veneer(s) carefully to remove any paper or adhesive which may have oozed through, and then lightly sand with O grade glasspaper.

If veneers are to be jointed (as in Fig. 153a) when using the press method, they must be cut exactly to size and stuck together with gummed paper tape or Sellotape before laying in the way already described. If very small pieces of veneer are used, as in marquetry work, all the pieces forming the pattern

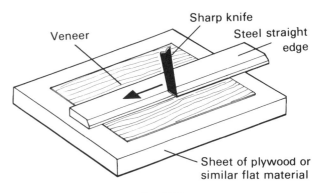

Veneer    Sharp knife    Steel straight edge

Sheet of plywood or similar flat material

Fig. 157

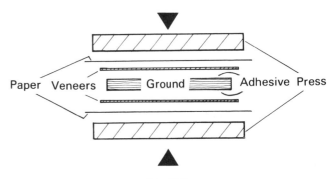

Paper  Veneers    Ground    Adhesive  Press

Fig. 158

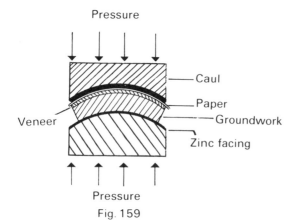

Fig. 159

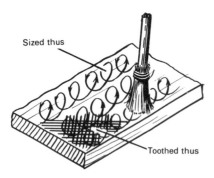

Fig. 160

Fig. 161

Fig. 162

should first be stuck face down on to a sheet of strong paper. This is then laid in the press as a single sheet of veneer, and the paper is scraped off after the adhesive has set.

## Veneering curved surfaces

Curved surfaces are veneered as above, but cauls (Fig. 159) are used in place of a flat press. Cauls are heavy blocks of wood, usually zinc faced, which exactly match the shape of the curved ground being veneered.

## The hammer method

Prepare as described on page 57, then size the ground with watered-down animal glue (Fig. 160) and leave to dry.

Step 1 **Laying**

The ground should be secured to the bench top which has previously been covered with old newspaper.

Step 2 Wet the outer face of the veneer and apply hot, thin freshly-made animal glue to the underside and to the ground.

Step 3 Place veneer in position and hammer, using a 'zig-zag' action along the grain only to squeeze the surplus glue from under the veneer (Fig. 161). Wipe off the surplus glue with a damp rag.

Step 4 The glue remaining under the veneer will now have 'jelled'. Wipe the surface of the veneer with a wet rag and then run a warm iron lightly over it to remelt the glue (Fig. 162).

SAFETY NOTE: *if you use an electric iron, first disconnect it from the power point.*

Step 5 Hammer again and repeat steps (4) and (5) until sure that the veneer has bedded down firmly on to the ground. Any unevenness or lumps can easily be found by running the finger tips over the surface.

Step 6 Wipe the veneered surface clean with a damp rag. Tape down any splits or edges which may curl on drying out and leave for at least a day before cleaning up.

Step 7 Turn the ground over and veneer the reverse side if necessary.

## Jointing veneers

Straight veneer joints are made like this, when using animal glue:

Step 1 Lay the first veneer A (Fig. 163a).

Step 2 Lay the second veneer B to overlap A by about 10 mm (Fig. 163b).

Step 3 Using a steel straight edge and a very sharp chisel or fine bladed knife, cut through both veneers with one stroke (Fig. 163c).

Step 4 Remove the waste piece of B, lift up the cut edge of B with a fine knife blade and pull out the waste edge of A, (Fig. 163d).

Step 5 Press the cut edge of B back into place, re-iron and hammer down.

Step 6 Tape the joint using gummed paper strip (Fig. 163e).

## Cross banding (Fig. 153b)

Lay cross-grained strips of veneer around the edge of a panel or other surfaces like this.

Step 1 Lay the main veneer as in Fig. 161, leaving an unveneered border of ground.

Step 2 Trim the edges of the veneer parallel to the edges of the ground with a cutting gauge (Fig. 164a), removing the surplus with a sharp chisel.

Step 3 Cut lengths of cross-grained veneer and lay them, using the back of a cross pene hammer (Fig. 164b). Stripey grained veneers are best for this purpose.

Step 4 Tape all joints.

Step 5 Clean up when dry.

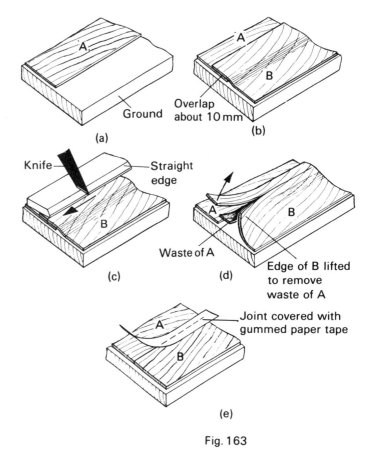

Fig. 163

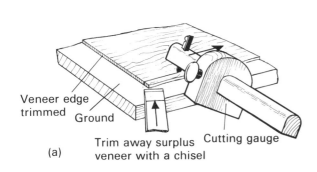

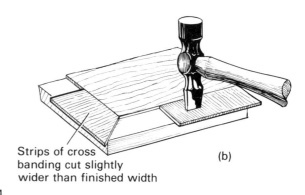

Fig. 164

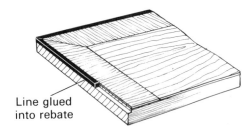

Line glued
into rebate

Fig. 165

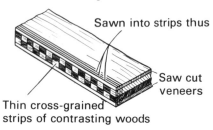

Sawn into strips thus

Saw cut
veneers

Thin cross-grained
strips of contrasting woods

Fig. 166

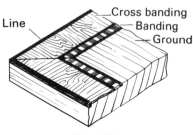

Cross banding
Banding
Ground
Line

Fig. 167

Fig. 168

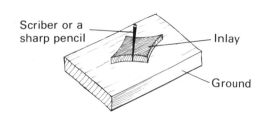

Scriber or a
sharp pencil

Inlay

Ground

Fig. 169 (a)

## Lines and bandings

A line (1 mm to 3 mm square) may be added around the outer edge of a veneer pattern (Fig. 165).

This is glued into a small rebate cut into the wood with a cutting gauge. The line is held in place until set by binding with tape or gummed paper strip. Lines, sometimes called 'strings', are bought in approximately 1 metre lengths as are bandings (built up patterns made as in Fig. 166). They may also be used as in Fig. 167.

If the main surface of the wood is not to be veneered, cross banding and lines are glued into a shallow rebate as shown.

## Inlay work

This consists of gluing small pieces of wood into a recess cut into the surface of the ground (Fig. 168).

Step 1 Cut the inlay shape from thin wood or thick veneer, hold it in place on the ground and carefully scribe round it (Fig. 169a).

Step 2 Cut the recess with chisels and gouges so that the inlay fits tightly into it (Fig. 169b). The inlay should stand slightly proud of the surface of the ground to allow for cleaning up.

Step 3 Glue the inlay into the recess as in Fig. 169c and clean up when set.

Lines may also be inlaid. A small groove is made in the ground with a scratch stock and the line glued into it (Fig. 170a and b).

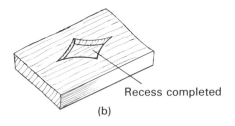

Recess completed

(b)

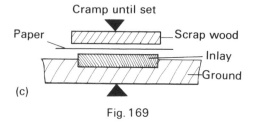

Cramp until set

Paper

Scrap wood

Inlay

Ground

(c)

Fig. 169

## DECORATIVE USE OF JOINTS

In addition to holding a job together, joints may also be used as a decorative feature. Fig. 171a, b and c, show examples of decorative bridle and halving joints, plain and wedged tenons, and dovetails.

In tenons, etc., (a) the joint is made and fitted but not glued up, an allowance being left for shaping when marking out; and (b) the amount that the tenon projects beyond the mortice is marked on with a pencil, the joint taken apart, and the shaping done with chisels and spokeshave before final assembly.

NOTE: *care must be taken not to damage the shaped end of the tenon when gluing and cramping up.*

In dovetails, great care must be taken in accurately spacing the tails and in cutting and fitting the fine pins.

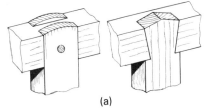

(a)

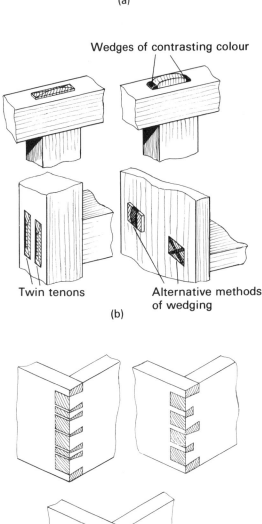

Wedges of contrasting colour

Twin tenons

Alternative methods of wedging

(b)

(c)

Fig. 171

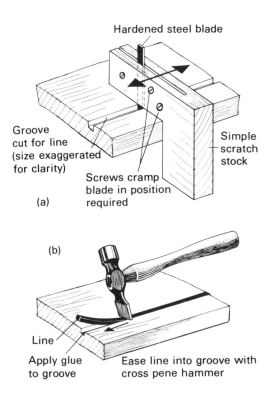

Hardened steel blade

Groove cut for line (size exaggerated for clarity)

Simple scratch stock

Screws cramp blade in position required

(a)

(b)

Line

Apply glue to groove

Ease line into groove with cross pene hammer

Fig. 170

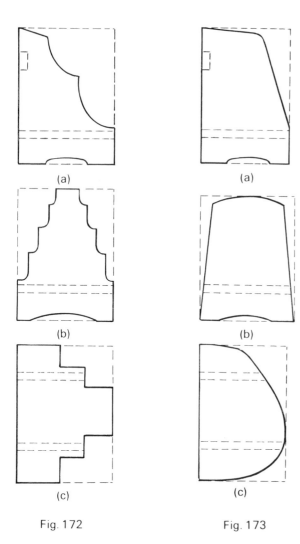

Fig. 172                Fig. 173

# SHAPING

The methods used in cutting shaped carcase ends, table tops, etc., are dealt with in Chapter 3. However, before any wood is cut away thought must be given to the appearance of the finished outline.

Shaping is carried out on woodwork:

(a) to reduce its weight without weakening it;

(b) to make it more convenient to use;

(c) to make it more pleasing to look at.

As (a) and (b) come more within the scope of planning and design than decoration, they are dealt with in Chapter 11.

Shaping for appearances' sake (c) should be done with restraint. Compare the book rack and book shelf end shapes shown in Fig. 172a, b and c with Fig. 173a, b and c. Notice that cutting away too much of the basic shape, or cutting it in a series of fussy steps and little curves, does not give a pleasant shape (Fig. 172a to c). Fig. 173a, b and c show shapes which are neither overcut nor fussy and as a result are more attractive to the eye. Note too the tapered legs, curved lower edges of rails, and simply shaped tops to tables and stools in Fig. 65.

The sharp edge of a piece of wood may also be shaped as a chamfer (Fig. 174a and b), or as a moulding (Fig. 175). By removing a little of the wood in this way harsh edges are 'softened' and made more attractive.

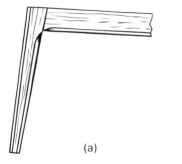
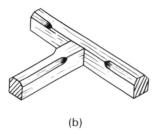

(a)              (b)

Fig. 174

## Chamfers

Chamfers (bevelled edges) are easily cut with a smoothing plane or spokeshave, or, where stopped, with a chisel. Fig. 176 shows different ways of stopping chamfers.

(a) The edges and ends of the chamfer are marked on with a sharp pencil. Do *not* use a marking gauge or the scratch mark will be left on the wood when the chamfer is cut.

(b) When chamfering with a chisel use a paring or slicing action to remove the wood as in Fig. 177a. Cut the stopped ends of the chamfer last, using the chisel bevel side downwards as in Fig. 177b. Work *with* the grain as far as possible. A good chamfer is sharp, clean cut, and not ragged or rounded at the edges.

## Mouldings

Mouldings such as that shown in Fig. 178 are not used on modern woodwork, simple shapes and sections being preferred. The legs of a stool may be made 'round-square' or oval in cross section (Fig. 179a and b). To ensure that this rounding is even along the leg, make a simple cardboard template with which to check it, (Fig. 180).

As with shaping in general, DO NOT REMOVE TOO MUCH WOOD (compare mouldings in Fig. 181a and b).

Fig. 175

Fig. 176

Edges of chamfer marked with pencil

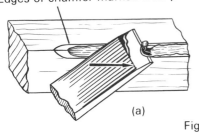

(a)

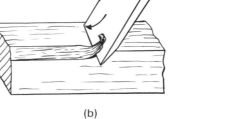

(b)

Fig. 177

Fig. 178

Corners well rounded

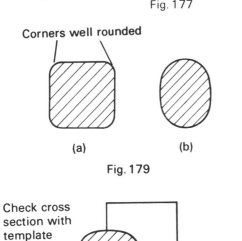

(a)          (b)

Fig. 179

Check cross section with template

Cardboard template

Fig. 180

Good          Bad

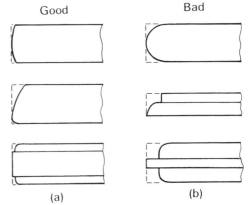

(a)          (b)

Fig. 181

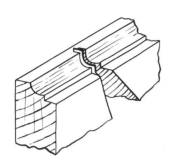

Fig. 182

Many mouldings may be worked with a smoothing plane, spokeshave and suitably shaped glasspapering block. Where mouldings are stepped (Fig. 175), a moulding plane with a specially shaped sole and blade (Fig. 182) may be used.

Alternatively the steps may be gauged and cut with rebate or shoulder planes and then finished off as before (Fig. 183a to d).

For small mouldings a scratch stock blade may be ground to suit the profile (shape) and used to complete the moulding (Fig. 184).

## SURFACE TOOLING (gouge work)

For many centuries woodwork was decorated by carving. Examples of such work are to be found in old churches (particularly on the choir stalls), in many old buildings, and on much antique furniture.

Today this type of carved decoration has largely gone out of fashion, but carved work in the form of 'treen' (carved dishes, bowls, etc.) and simply carved ornaments are very popular. The production of such work is described in Chapter 5.

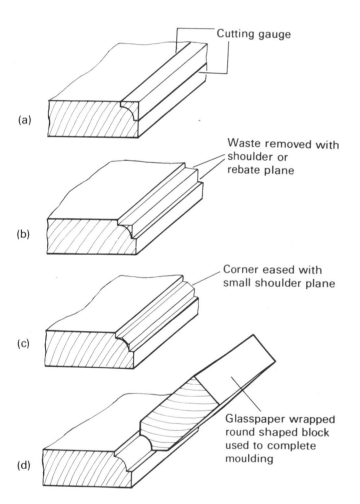

(a)    Cutting gauge

(b)    Waste removed with shoulder or rebate plane

(c)    Corner eased with small shoulder plane

(d)    Glasspaper wrapped round shaped block used to complete moulding

Fig. 183

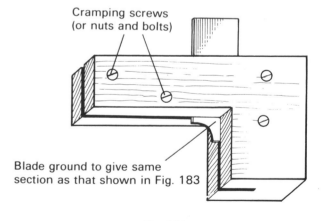

Cramping screws (or nuts and bolts)

Blade ground to give same section as that shown in Fig. 183

Fig. 184

# 5 Carving

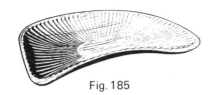

Fig. 185

## TOOLS

Carving, examples of which are shown in Figs. 185 to 187 and 195f and g, 196f and 201g, is carried out with gouges and chisels, and to a lesser extent with the occasional use of saws and rasps (woodworkers' files) spokeshaves, shaped scrapers and glasspaper.

### Gouges

These are made in a number of shapes and sizes; Fig. 188a to d show a few of the possible forms available. Gouges are usually ground from the outside (firmer) or the inside (scribing), but some gouges used in carving are ground equally from inside and outside (Fig. 189). The grinding angle is lower than that of a normal chisel; this gives an easier cutting action.

Fig. 186

Fig. 187

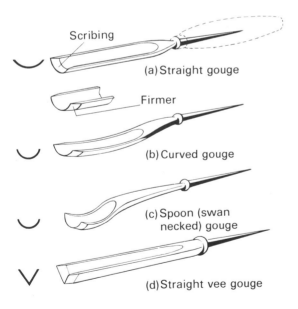

Scribing

(a) Straight gouge

Firmer

(b) Curved gouge

(c) Spoon (swan necked) gouge

(d) Straight vee gouge

Fig. 188

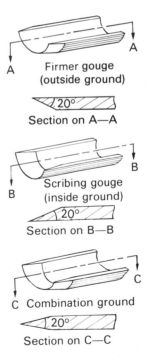

Firmer **gouge** (outside ground)

20°

Section on A—A

Scribing gouge (inside ground)

20°

Section on B—B

C Combination ground

20°

Section on C—C

Fig. 189

Fig. 190

Chisels and gouges used for carving must be honed to a very keen edge, and a much finer grade of oilstone must be used than when sharpening edge tools for ordinary bench work. 'Arkansas' and 'Washita' stones are recommended, and the whole of the ground bevel is honed not just the tip which is usual when sharpening plane blades and chisels (see Fig. 287b).

An oilstone slip is used to remove the burr from the inside face of the cutting edge of gouges. A leather strop may be used to give an even finer cutting edge.

Protect the cutting edge of carving tools by keeping them in a cloth tool-roll when not in use.

An ordinary mallet can be used to strike the gouge, but a round-headed carver's mallet is preferable (Fig. 190).

### Rasps
To remove any surface imperfection left by the gouges, rasps and Surform rasps are used for external curves (Figs. 191 and 338) and 'rifflers' (double-ended rasps having curved cutting faces) for internal shapes (Fig. 192).

Fig. 191

### Scrapers
When making a simple wooden dish (see Fig. 195g) a shaped scraper (Fig. 193) is useful for final trueing of any surface where the grain is at all twisty.

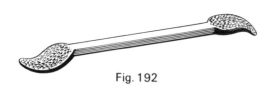

Fig. 192

## DISHES AND PLATTERS (TREEN)
### Selecting the wood
To make a dish similar to that shown in Fig. 195f, first choose a suitable piece of softish hardwood which has a decorative grain. Cherry or Honduras mahogany are ideal timbers, but at first avoid hard timbers such as oak, sycamore, or teak, and difficult timbers such as twisty grained elm.

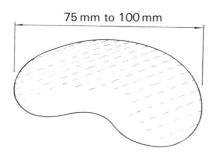

75 mm to 100 mm

Fig. 193

### The shape
Provided the dish is big enough to do its job satisfactorily, its shape is a matter of personal choice. Leaves, shells, fish and other natural shapes are effective, but attractive shapes can often be produced by 'doodling' (see Fig. 194a to g).

## Cutting (inside shape)

Step 1  Draw the shape on the wood, cut out with a bow saw, and true up with spokeshave and rasps (Fig. 195a).

Step 2  Cramp work to the bench and hollow the inside, using gouges and mallet (Fig. 195b). Start the cuts about 6 mm in from the outer edge, and do not hollow too deeply. Try to obtain a cross section like Fig. 195c rather than Fig. 195d.

Cut with and across the grain but not against or into it. This is likely to tear the grain badly or lead to overcutting or splitting.

Step 3  Go over the hollowed block to remove uneven preliminary gouge cuts using gouges and then rifflers. Work back to the outer edge.

Step 4  Clean up the internal shape with scraper and glasspaper, using $1\frac{1}{2}$ grade followed by O grade (Fig. 195e).

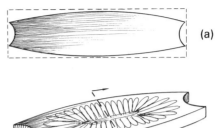

(a)

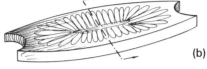

(b)

Right    (c)

Wrong    (d)

(e)

(f)

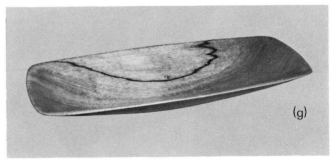

(g)

Fig. 195

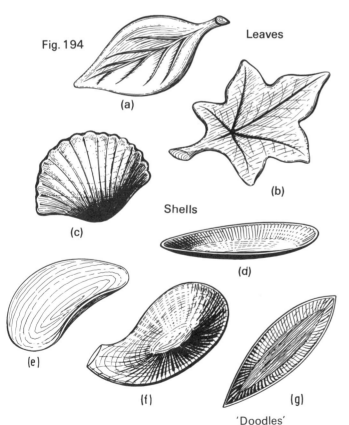

Fig. 194

Leaves

(a)

(b)

Shells

(c)

(d)

(e)

(f)

(g)

'Doodles'

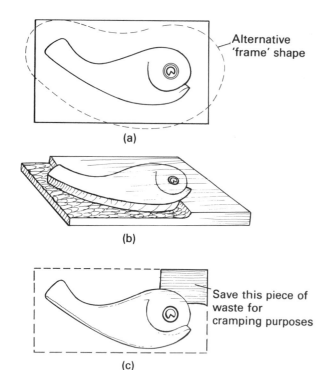

Alternative 'frame' shape

(a)

(b)

Save this piece of waste for cramping purposes

(c)

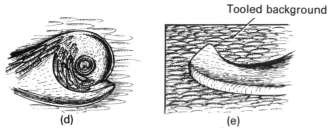

Tooled background

(d)                    (e)

(f)

Fig. 196

## Cutting (outside shape)

Turn block over to shape the outside, using spokeshave, broad bladed chisels and rasps. Finally, clean up the surface with glasspaper.

NOTE: *care must be taken not to cramp the hollowed dish too tightly to the bench as this may cause it to crack. Packing the inside under the cramp will help to avoid splitting.*

*The external lines of the dish should follow those of the inside shape, and the edge of the rim should be fined down to prevent any feeling of heaviness.*

## Finish

Apply a suitable finish (see Chapter 7). As with most decorative woodwork a smooth satin finish rather than a high gloss is preferable.

The wooden spoon and fork in Fig. 195f are made in a broadly similar way. The outline is cut out, the spoon bowl shaped, and finally the handle is rounded off.

## 'BAS RELIEF' CARVING

The raised decorative plaque shown in Fig. 196f is carved as follows:

Step 1 Prepare a full-sized outline sketch, keeping the outlines and details simple and clean cut (Fig. 196a).

Step 2 Trace or copy the outline and main details on to the wood. Gouge away the waste wood from around the outline if the rectangular shape of the block is to be kept as a frame or background (Fig. 196b), or saw around the outline and trim with gouges and chisels if a 'silhouette' is required (Fig. 196c).

Step 3 Cramp the work to the bench. Shape the work to the cross sections required, roughing it out with chisels and gouges, then smoothing up with rifflers and glasspaper (Fig. 196d).

Step 4 If a 'wavy' background is required, this may be suggested by light, nearly horizontal, gouge cuts (Fig. 196e). Other textured effects may be similarly produced.

Step 5 Polish.

NOTE: *if a naturalistic subject is chosen for the carving, avoid trying to show every little detail. Absolute accuracy is not essential, a simplified general form being more important.*

## THREE-DIMENSIONAL WORK

This is the most advanced and most difficult type of carving. The subject may be a natural form (either animal or plant), or an interesting abstract shape suggested may be by a piece of weathered rock from the sea shore, an unusually twisted branch of a tree, or just a flight of fancy (Figs. 197 to 200).

While the final form of the sculpture can never be accurately shown in a drawing, preliminary sketches (Fig. 201b) are necessary to ensure that the proportions and balance are right. From the sketches, a clay or plasticine model may be made which will give a clearer impression of the finished shape.

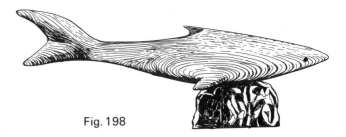

Fig. 198

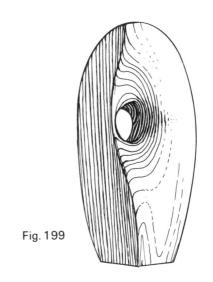

Fig. 199

Fig. 197

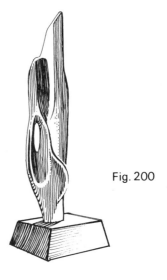

Fig. 200

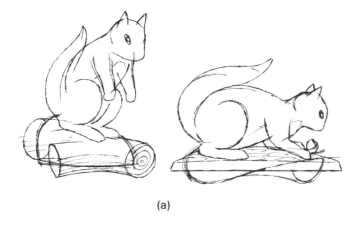

(a)

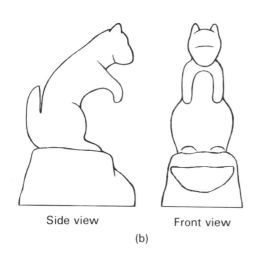

Side view        Front view

(b)

The method of carving the simplified figure shown in Fig. 201g is as follows. (Early practices should be carved out of an even-grained softwood such as yellow pine or a soft hardwood such as lime.)

Step 1 From the preliminary sketches, prepare front and side (end) views (Fig. 201b).

Step 2 Copy or trace one view (the more difficult one) on to the wood and cut roughly to shape (Fig. 201c).

Step 3 Draw the other view on to the cut surface and saw and chisel out as in Fig. 201d. This will give a 'square figure'.

(It is often a good plan to mount the figure on to a base of scrap wood which can be gripped in the vice or held down on the bench – see Fig. 201e.)

Step 4 Continue working with gouges, chisels and rifflers to give the figure its true shape when viewed from all sides. Fig. 201f shows one part being rounded off.

Remember that it is the general impression the sculpture creates which is important. Good simple form and a satisfying 'feel' to the finished work are of far greater value than too much attention to details. Use can often be made of the contour effect caused by the strongly-marked growth rings found in some timbers.

Fig. 201h shows another piece of three-dimensional work, at Step 4 above.

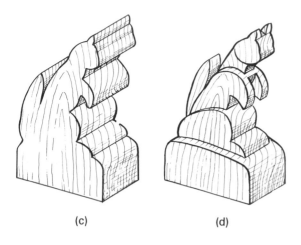

(c)                    (d)

Fig. 201

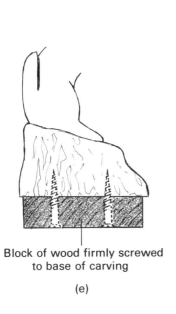

Block of wood firmly screwed
to base of carving

(e)

(g)

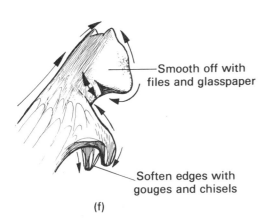

Smooth off with
files and glasspaper

Soften edges with
gouges and chisels

(f)

Fig. 201                              (h)

# 6 Lathe Work

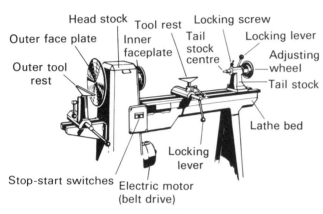

Head stock
Tool rest
Locking screw
Outer face plate
Inner faceplate
Tail stock centre
Locking lever
Adjusting wheel
Outer tool rest
Tail stock
Lathe bed
Stop-start switches
Electric motor (belt drive)
Locking lever

Fig. 202

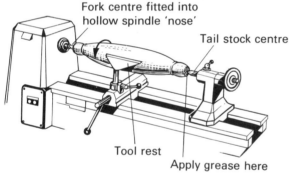

Fork centre fitted into hollow spindle 'nose'
Tail stock centre
Tool rest
Apply grease here

Fig. 203 (a)

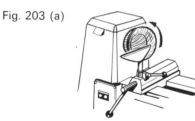

Fig. 203 (b)

(a)      (b)

Fig. 205

Fig. 202 shows the main parts of a modern wood-turning lathe, on which work is turned either,

(a) between centres (Fig. 203a and the stem of the table lamp shown in Fig. 204), or

(b) on a faceplate (Fig. 203b, the base of the lamp in Fig. 204, and the bowl shown in Fig. 216a). Work of large diameter may be turned on the outside face plate (Fig. 202).

## TURNING BETWEEN CENTRES

Turn a lamp stem (see Fig. 204), a turned leg, or other similarly-shaped work as follows.

Step 1 *Selection*

Choose a suitable piece of timber. Softwoods and hardwoods may both be turned, but hardwoods with attractive grain markings (oak, walnut, elm, cherry, mahogany, etc.) give a more pleasing result. The wood *must* be free from splits and large or loose knots as these will spoil the look of the work and, more seriously, may cause an accident during turning.

Fig. 204

**Step 2** *Preparation*

Find the centre of both ends of the wood as in Fig. 205a and plane off the sharp corners to give an approximately octagonal (eight-sided) shape as in Fig. 205b.

Drive the fork centre (Fig. 206a) into one end of the wood, positioning the prongs so that they do not cause a split, and drill or bradawl a small hole in the centre of the other end to take the tailstock centre (Fig. 206b).

**Step 3** *Setting up*

Mount the work on the lathe as in Fig. 203a, putting a little heavy grease or wax on to the tip of the tailstock centre before inserting it into the hole. From time to time during turning, check that the tailstock centre is fitting tightly up to the wood. If too tight it will cause scorching, if too slack the wood may fly off the lathe.

Position the tool rest close to the work and rotate the wood by hand *before* switching on, to ensure that it will fully clear the rest.

**Step 4** *Cutting*

(a) *The use of the gouge* A turning gouge (Fig. 207a) has a heavier blade and longer handle than an ordinary firmer gouge (Fig. 285). Its cutting edge is ground to an angle of about 40° and does not have a second 'honing' angle like a standard chisel or gouge. This is because when in use the bevel should rub on the side of the work (Fig. 208). To make the gouge cut, the handle, which should be tucked into the right side of the waist or hip, is slightly raised. This causes the tip of the gouge to 'bite' very slightly, thus peeling off the surface of the wood (rather like unwinding a 'Swiss roll' cake). Be careful *not* to jab the gouge into the work or severe damage will be caused.

(b) *Roughing down* Hold the gouge with the left hand on top of the blade where it lies on the tool rest and the right hand gripping the lower end of the handle, and take a series of light cuts until the wood is reduced to a cylinder. Roughly taper the cylinder at this stage if required.

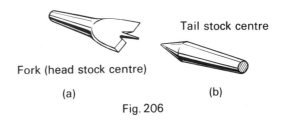

Tail stock centre

Fork (head stock centre)

(a)                                    (b)

Fig. 206

(a)  Turning gouge (note strong blade and long handle)

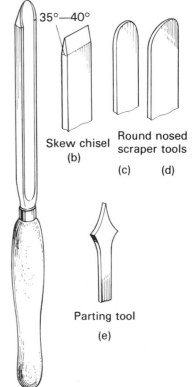

35°—40°

Skew chisel
(b)

Round nosed scraper tools

(c)        (d)

Parting tool
(e)

Fig. 207

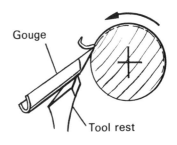

Gouge

Tool rest

Fig. 208

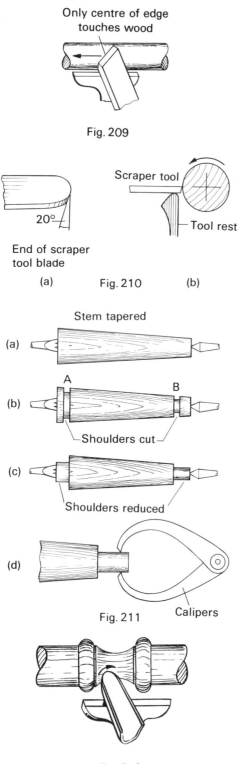

Only centre of edge
touches wood

Fig. 209

End of scraper
tool blade

20°

Scraper tool

Tool rest

(a)          Fig. 210          (b)

Stem tapered

(a)

A          B

(b)

Shoulders cut

(c)

Shoulders reduced

(d)

Fig. 211          Calipers

Fig. 212

(c) *Smoothing and finishing off* Because of its shape, it is very difficult to obtain an even straight-sided cylinder with a turning gouge. To finish off (as for the lamp stem), a skew chisel is used (Fig. 207b). This is ground equally from both sides, and, as with the gouge, the bevel should rub on the face of the wood – see Fig. 209.

As this is a rather difficult technique to master, it may be preferable to scrape the surface smooth. For this a strong 25 mm firmer chisel may be used (ground as in Fig. 210a). Hold it so that the top face of the blade is horizontal (or slightly inclined downwards) and level with the centre line of the work (Fig. 210b).

If making a lamp stem, after tapering as in Fig. 211a, mark off the actual length required and the position of the 'shoulder' by holding a pencil against the revolving work. Cut the shoulders A and B with a parting tool (Fig. 211b). Then using a scraper tool, reduce the diameter of the 'joint' part of the work as in Fig. 211c, checking the diameter with calipers (Fig. 211d) – about 20 mm to 25 mm diameter with a 3 mm shoulder would be satisfactory.

Give the surface a final smoothing using medium and fine grades of glasspaper. Do not use coarse grades as these will scratch the surface badly.

SAFETY NOTE: *when glasspapering or polishing, first remove the tool rest or you may trap your fingers.*

Concave curves are roughed out with gouges, working, as always in wood turning, from the thicker to the thinner part of the wood. Fig. 212 shows how this is done using a slight 'swinging' action.

Turned handles and knobs, like some of those shown in Fig. 150, can be conveniently turned as in Fig. 213. It is quicker and more convenient to turn a set of knobs from one length of wood (as shown) than to turn each one on its own. A template should be made to check that each knob is turned exactly the same size and shape.

(d) *Polishing* Work may be easily polished on the lathe using white polish to fill the grain, and rubbing down with 00 grade glasspaper ('flour' paper) before wax polishing (see Chapter 7).

(e) *Parting off* This is carried out with either a parting tool (Fig. 207e) or a strong mortice chisel.

SAFETY NOTE: *the lathe should be set to a fairly slow speed before parting off. The lower speeds should also be used for large diameter work, as high speeds are likely to cause it to fly off the lathe. This may cause serious injury. Heavy tool pressure must also be avoided as this is likely to cause the work to split or again may force it off the lathe.*

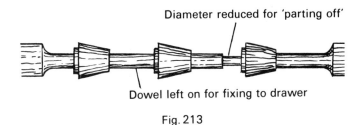

Diameter reduced for 'parting off'

Dowel left on for fixing to drawer

Fig. 213

## Wooden disc chucks

Sometimes, as with a stool leg having a square top end, it is advisable to replace the fork centre with a simple wooden disc chuck (Fig. 214). A hardwood disc about 25 mm thick is turned on a faceplate (see below) and then a square hole is cut in its centre, into which the top of the leg is fitted.

Step 5 *Boring holes*

The stem of the lampstand will require drilling to take the wire before parting off. While it is possible to drill short holes after the work has been removed from the lathe, the best way to bore such a hole down the centre is to use a special boring attachment (Fig. 215).

This attachment which is clamped in the tool rest holder acts as a tail stock centre, and a specially designed auger bit passes through this into the wood. With the work revolving at about 750 revolutions per minute, hold the auger handle firmly and push the bit gently into the wood. To avoid any possibility of the auger becoming jammed in the wood, withdraw it to clear the chips after a few inches have been bored. Repeat this as often as is found necessary until the hole has been bored right through the centre of the work.

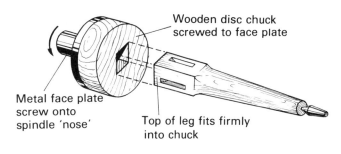

Wooden disc chuck screwed to face plate

Metal face plate screw onto spindle 'nose'

Top of leg fits firmly into chuck

Fig. 214

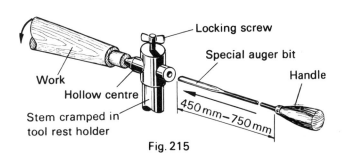

Locking screw

Special auger bit

Handle

Work

Hollow centre

Stem cramped in tool rest holder

450 mm–750 mm

Fig. 215

(a)

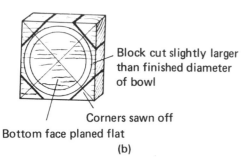

Block cut slightly larger
than finished diameter
of bowl

Corners sawn off

Bottom face planed flat

(b)

Fig. 216

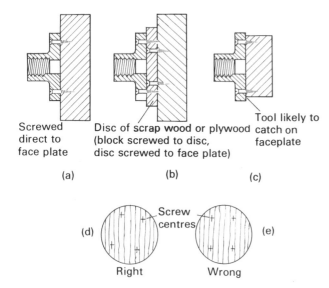

Screwed
direct to
face plate

(a)

Disc of scrap wood or plywood
(block screwed to disc,
disc screwed to face plate)

(b)

Tool likely to
catch on
faceplate

(c)

Screw
centres

(d)    (e)

Right    Wrong

Fig. 217

## FACE PLATE TURNING

The shallow bowl shown in Fig. 216a was turned
from 38 mm thick English walnut whose close
decorative grain readily lends itself to work of this
type.

Step 1 *Preparation and mounting*

Mark out and saw off the corners as in Fig.
216b. The block of wood to be turned can be
screwed directly to the metal faceplate (Fig.
217a), but generally it is better to fit an
intermediate block as in Fig. 217b. This will
prevent any possibility of the tool catching on
the revolving faceplate (particularly if the
block is of small diameter, as in Fig. 217c),
and also ensure a good 'bed' for the
faceplate.

Screws of as thick a shank as possible
should be used to give the strongest grip on
the wood, and should be arranged so that no
two screws are in line along the grain (Fig.
217d and e).

Step 2 *Turning*

(a) *Single chucking* Suitable for the base of
the lamp in Fig. 204 and for some bowls.
(i) Turn the outside shape of the bowl as in
Fig. 218a. The tool rest must be moved from
time to time so that the cutting tools are
correctly supported. Remember to work from
the larger towards the smaller diameter as
indicated.
(ii) Turn the inside of the bowl, again
adjusting the position of the tool rest as
required (Fig. 218b). Considerable care will
be required when using a gouge for inside
work, so unless the worker has achieved a
fair degree of turning skill it may be safer to
use the scraper tool throughout this stage.
Do not hollow the bowl too deeply or the
tips of the holding screws will be 'bared',
thus spoiling the appearance of the completed
job – as well as blunting the cutting tools.

The lamp base should first be turned as in
Fig. 219. Then the hole for the stem is either
cut in with a narrow scraping tool (a strong
mortice chisel will do), or bored out with a
screwed (improved) centre bit or Jennings
bit of suitable diameter.

To avoid having screw holes in the base a *small* block may be secured (see Fig. 220) by gluing to a turned wooden disc, a piece of strong paper being placed between the work and the disc. Pressure must be maintained by means of G cramps until the glue is quite set.

(b) *Double chucking* In this method the outside is again turned first, but the work is mounted as in Fig. 221a and then reversed so that the inside of the bowl may be hollowed. To ensure exact centring when reversing the block, the base of the bowl can be fitted into an accurately-cut recess in the wood disc (Fig. 221b).

There are many tricks to the wood turner's trade; for details of more advanced work the books listed on page 168 should be consulted.

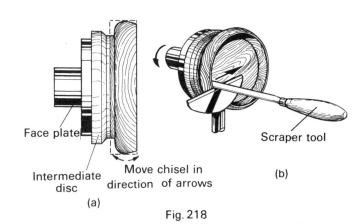

Fig. 218

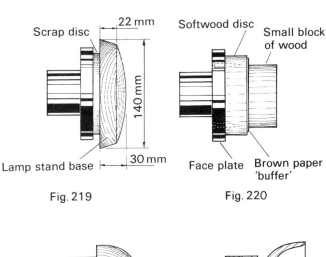

Fig. 219          Fig. 220

## SAFETY PRECAUTIONS

Accidents on the lathe can be very serious ones and must be avoided at all costs. The following simple rules must be obeyed.

(a) Make sure you know how and where to
    SWITCH OFF *BEFORE* you SWITCH ON.
(b) Before switching on:
    (i)   be certain that the wood is firmly secured to the faceplate or between centres;
    (ii)  revolve the work by hand to be sure that it completely clears the tool rest and lathe bed;
    (iii) check the speed setting (do not use too high a speed for wood of large diameter).
(c) Roll up your sleeves and tuck in your tie. If these should catch in the work a serious accident would occur.
(d) Never interfere with or distract the operator's attention while the lathe is switched on.
(e) Always wear a face shield or visor when turning or machine sanding, to protect your eyes from flying wood chips or dust. Avoid breathing the dust by wearing a simple throw-away dust mask.

Detailed safety precautions concerning the use of other powered woodworking equipment are given in Chapter 10.

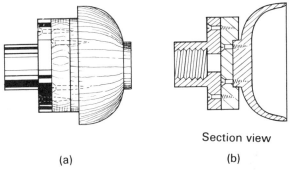

Fig. 221

# 7 Finishes

The surface of untreated indoor woodwork soon becomes dirty in use, so it is usual to apply a finish which both protects and improves its appearance.

## SURFACE PREPARATION

Before applying paints, varnishes, or polishes, the surface of the wood must be made quite smooth. After cleaning up with a smoothing plane, a scraper (see Fig. 336) may be used to level any tears in the grain. Finish off by using glasspaper or other abrasive coated paper round a cork block or rubber (Fig. 111).

Glasspaper is graded as follows, beginning with the finest grade: 00, 0, 1, $1\frac{1}{2}$, F2, M2, $2\frac{1}{2}$, 3. The 00 grade is often known as 'flour' paper. The two most widely-used grades are $1\frac{1}{2}$ (a medium cut), followed by 0 grade (fine).

Garnet-paper, made by sticking powdered garnet (a naturally-occurring semi-precious stone) to paper, is harder-wearing than glasspaper.

Harder wearing still is aluminium oxide coated abrasive paper, which is used for power sanding (see page 131). The adhesive used to stick this type of abrasive to its backing-paper is usually waterproof, and aluminium oxide coated abrasive paper is known as 'wet or dry'. When very fine grades are used for smoothing painted or cellulosed surfaces, water is used as a lubricant, and this prevents the 'wet or dry' from becoming clogged, as well as imparting a much smoother, almost scratch free, surface to the finish.

A number grading system is used for aluminium oxide abrasive papers. The table gives a selection of useful grades.

| 400 | 240 | 150 | 100 | 50 |
|---|---|---|---|---|
| extra fine | finishing | fine | medium | coarse |
| 'wet or dry' for | | for preparing wood surfaces | | |
| painted surfaces | | | | |

Both garnet and aluminium oxide coated papers are more expensive than glasspaper.

If a clear finish (varnish, french polish, etc.) is to be applied, the surface must be glasspapered *along* the grain only, to avoid making fine scratches, but for painted surfaces a diagonal or circular movement is better.

An even smoother surface may be obtained by wiping the previously glasspapered surface with a wet rag. This raises the grain. Allow the surface to dry and then glasspaper again, using 0 or 00 grade.

## CHOICE OF FINISH

The finish to be applied will depend on (a) the type of wood used, and (b) the purpose of the finished article (Fig. 222 gives some suggestions).

Occasionally wood is stained to improve its colour; details are given on pages 84–5. If staining is required, it is done before the finish is applied.

## WOOD FINISHES

| FINISH | SOLVENT | Suitable for INside or OUTside use | EXAMPLES OF USE | |
|---|---|---|---|---|
| **French polish** | Methylated spirits | IN | Hardwood furniture – will NOT withstand heat or damp | |
| **Wax polish** | Turpentine or white spirit | IN | Any polished or varnished woodwork | |
| **Sealers** | Turpentine or white spirit | IN (some OUT) | Flush plywood doors, floors furniture | |
| **Varnish** | Turpentine or white spirit | IN and OUT | Skirtings and inside woodwork, hardwood doors and gates, boats | |
| **Cellulose lacquers** | Cellulose thinners | IN and OUT | Clear: hardwood/kitchen furniture<br>Coloured: toys, bathroom fittings and furniture | |
| **Gloss paints** | Turpentine or white spirit (paraffin for cleaning off) | IN and OUT | Softwood joinery – window frames, skirtings, etc. | |
| **Polyurethane** | — | IN and OUT | Clear: any attractively grained wood<br>Coloured: kitchen and garden furniture | heat and damp resistant, therefore suitable for boats, etc. |
| **Linseed oil** | Turpentine or white spirit | IN | If used outside, work soon becomes very dirty; used as preliminary treatment for some hardwoods | |
| **Teak oil** | Turpentine or white spirit | IN (some OUT) | Teak or similar furniture and fittings, gives dull or lustre finish withstands heat and damp | |
| **Creosote** | Paraffin | OUT only | Fencing and garden posts; sheds | |
| **Commercial preservatives** | Paraffin | OUT | Exposed cedarwood boarding, fences, sheds, etc. | |

Fig. 222

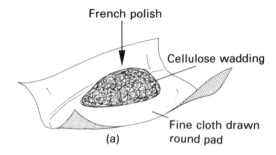

French polish

Cellulose wadding

Fine cloth drawn round pad

(a)

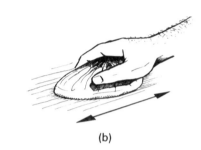

(b)

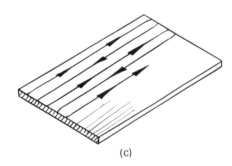

(c)

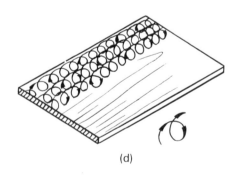

(d)

Fig. 223

## French polish

French polish is made by dissolving shellac in methylated spirit. Button polish, a deep brown colour, is used for polishing dark woods such as mahogany. Garnet polish is a lighter shade, and white polish (brush polish) made from bleached shellac is used for light-coloured timbers such as oak, chestnut, or beech.

Soak a pad of cellulose wadding or cotton wool with the polish, and squeeze out any surplus. Then cover the pad with a piece of lint-free cloth – linen, or fine cotton (Fig. 223a and b).

Rub the pad lightly along the grain, overlapping each stroke (Fig. 223c). After a few courses (a 'course' is a series of strokes which covers the whole surface) the surface will become tacky. Allow it to dry off and then repeat the process.

When a layer of polish has been built up, courses of circular strokes (Fig. 223d) will 'pull over' the polish to fill the pores in the grain. Always finish off with straight strokes.

When the polish has thoroughly hardened, lightly 'flat' it (rub it down) with 00 grade glasspaper to remove the high gloss which may look like a streaky varnish finish.

Repeat the process until the required depth of polish has been obtained. Brush polish may be applied with a soft 'mop' (brush) used to float on an even coat along the grain. This filler coat is cut down with 00 grade glasspaper and is usually followed up by wax polishing.

## Wax polish

Wax polish is made from bees wax which is dissolved in turpentine. A little polish is applied to the wood and rubbed hard with a dry rag until a dull sheen is obtained.

NOTE:
(a) *Wax polish is best applied over a cut-down coat of brush polish which prevents the wax from sinking too far into the surface of the wood.*
(b) *Apply only a very little wax polish at a time – too much will result in a dull, sticky finish which easily shows finger marks.*

## Wood sealer

Commercially-produced sealers are easy to use, being applied evenly to floors, doors and furniture with a rag, sponge, or brush. Between coats, the surface should be rubbed down with wire wool and the final coat should be a thin one. This gives a hard wearing finish which brings out the grain of the timber.

## Varnish

Varnishes should be applied with a very clean brush and flowed out on to the grain, finishing with light strokes from end to end of the work. They are equally suitable for inside or outside use, but most tend to darken the colour of the wood slightly. Special varnishes are available for boat work, etc.

NOTE: *do not apply varnish, paint, or any other finish in a dusty place, or 'nibs' will form around dust which settles on the wet surface.*

## Cellulose lacquer

These lacquers, like model aeroplane 'dope', or nail varnish, dry quickly and set hard in about an hour to give a tough glossy finish which is fairly heat resistant.

Clear lacquers are suitable for use on trays and hardwood surfaces, etc., to give a natural finish, and coloured lacquers are often used for finishing toys and kitchen and bathroom furniture.

Because they dry so rapidly, lacquers must not be brushed in like gloss paints (see below), but should be flowed on to the surface from a full soft-bristled brush.

## Gloss paints

Gloss paint is the standard finish for inside and outside joinery – windows, doors, etc. It is applied in three layers.

**Knotting and priming** The purpose of priming paint is to key (stick) the coats which follow to the wood. Before priming, all knots must be coated with 'knotting' (shellac varnish) to prevent natural oils and resins 'weeping' through the finished paint surface.

Priming paint is fairly runny and must be well brushed into the grain (Fig. 224).

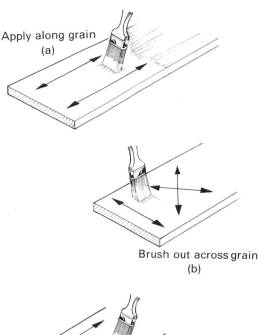

Apply along grain
(a)

Brush out across grain
(b)

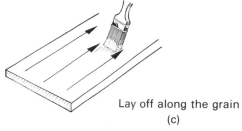

Lay off along the grain
(c)

Fig. 224

**Undercoating** Smooth off any nibs with glasspaper and apply undercoat of the correct colour; give one or two coats, allowing each to dry overnight. Undercoat gives 'body' to the paint film or skin. Lightly glasspaper again if required.

**Finishing coat** Brush on the top or gloss coat as in Fig. 224. This final coat contains varnish and puts the protective shine on the painted surface.

## General note on brushes and paint preparation

1 Between coats of the *same* paint or varnish, brushes may be kept in a jar or tin of water (Fig. 225a).

2 If a small hole is drilled through the handle, the brush may be hung (Fig. 225b) to prevent any bending of the bristles.

3 Between coats of *different* paints or varnishes, the brush *must* be washed out in the correct solvent (see Fig. 222).

4 When the work is finished, after cleaning in solvent wash the brush in detergent or soap and water and allow to dry, before putting it away.

   Good brushes are expensive and deserve good treatment. A sticky brush is useless.

5 Unless the paint is thixotropic (non-drip) it must be well stirred before use, until there are no lumps or sediment left at the bottom of the tin.

6 If the paint is too thick, stir in a *small* amount of turpentine or white spirit (turpentine substitute).

## Polyurethane lacquer

Polyurethane lacquers are somewhat similar to synthetic resin glues because they set by chemical action, not just by drying out.

   Their chief advantage over other finishes is that they will stand up better to outside weather conditions and are highly wear and heat resistant.

   Three or four coats are usually needed to obtain a good thickness of the finish, either clear or coloured.

NOTE:

(*a*) *The maker's instructions must be carefully followed as some types of polyurethane lacquer have to be prepared by mixing the contents of two tins, while others are ready mixed.*

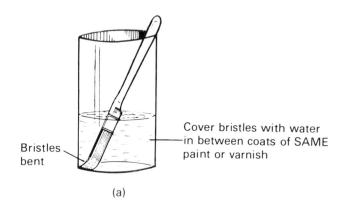

Bristles bent

Cover bristles with water in between coats of SAME paint or varnish

(a)

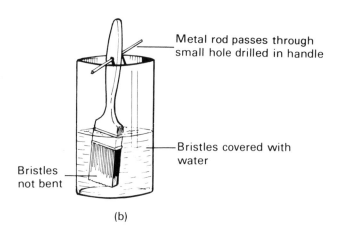

Metal rod passes through small hole drilled in handle

Bristles covered with water

Bristles not bent

(b)

Fig. 225

(b) *If a clear 'satin' finish is wanted, the final coat should be lightly rubbed along the grain with fine grade 'wet or dry' abrasive paper, using water as a lubricant. For a finer finish, buff the surface with cellulose 'rubbing down' compound such as is used when re-spraying cars.*

## Linseed oil

This is obtained from the flax plant and when exposed to the air hardens to form a tough skin. It should therefore *never* be used as a lubricant for oilstones.

Apart from its use as a preservative when rubbed into the blades of cricket bats, linseed oil can be applied to the surface of oak and other light-coloured timbers to bring out the grain.

When the oil has been well rubbed in and allowed to dry, brush polish can be applied as previously described. Linseed oil should not be used for oiling outside woodwork such as oak front doors or gates; it attracts dust which will soon cause the work to look dirty.

## Teak oil

While linseed oil will bring out the grain of decorative hardwoods, teak oil, a commercial preparation, is often preferred when a matt (dull) or lustre finish is required. Timbers such as afrormosia and African walnut are treated in this way, as well as teak. Different grades are available for inside and outside use.

Apply a good coat of oil to the bare wood with a clean soft rag, and allow it to soak into the wood for about ten minutes. Then wipe the surface with a dry rag to remove any surplus oil. Allow to dry overnight.

If a second coat is needed, first smooth the dry oiled surface with 00 grade glasspaper, wiping off any dust before applying the second coat.

## STAINS

The uninteresting grain or weak colour of some timbers may be improved by staining *before* varnishing, french polishing, etc.

Stains are generally water, spirit, or oil soluble.

**Water stains**

These are made up simply by dissolving the stain crystals or powder in hot water. Try out the stain on a spare piece of wood similar to that to be stained. Rub plenty of stain on to the surface and wipe off the surplus with a dry rag (the colour while still wet is the colour when polished). If required, thin down the stain with more water until a suitable shade is obtained and apply to the work.

As water stains tend to raise the grain (giving rise to 'white spotting' after rubbing down), the surface should be prepared as previously described on page 78–9.

Water stains will not take on greasy surfaces, but lead to patchiness and uneven colouring.

**Oil stains** (soluble in turpentine or naptha)
These do not have the drawbacks of water stains and are obtainable in a number of ready-mixed shades. They are, however, more costly.

Before wax polishing, oil stains must be 'fixed' with a coat of white french polish to prevent the wax solvent removing some of the stain from the surface.

## STAINS

| TYPE OF STAIN | SOLVENT | ADVANTAGES | DISADVANTAGES | EXAMPLES OF USE |
|---|---|---|---|---|
| **Water** | Water (best dissolved in very hot water) | Cheap, easy to make up | Will not take on greasy surfaces; raises the grain | For furniture, softwood flooring |
| **Oil** | Naptha, turpentine, white spirit | Purchased ready mixed; easily diluted or inter-mixed; does not raise grain; will take on slightly greasy woods | More expensive than water stains; wax polish will 'pick up' unless sealed with brush polish | For hardwood furniture and fittings |
| **Spirit** | Methylated spirits | Wide range of colours – in black, gives intense colouring to wood | Dries out very quickly, therefore patchy on large surfaces | For 'ebonising' furniture, coloured building bricks and toys, and tinting french polish |
| **Chemical:** Ammonia | Water | Gives 'fumed' finish | Fumes unpleasant and slow-acting | Mainly for oak furniture |
| Potassium-permanganate | Water | Deepens colour | Fades | For flooring and cheap woodwork |
| Potassium-bichromate | Water | Deepens hardwood colours | Poisonous | For mahogany and similar woods |

Fig. 226

**Spirit stains** (soluble in methylated spirits)
Spirit stain powders are easily dissolved in methylated spirits, and bright colours as well as wood shades are obtainable.

Black spirit stain which soaks well into the wood is ideal for 'ebonising' fine grained timbers such as mahogany, birch, or beech. If a little of the same stain powder is added to white french polish, this will make a black polish with which to complete the process.

### Chemical stains

Some stains which colour wood by chemical action are:

1 *Ammonia* which gives a fumed oak finish. The job is put in an airtight box with a dish containing strong '880' ammonia solution. The ammonia fumes cause the oak to turn a grey brown colour which, when rubbed with linseed oil, takes on a rich brown shade. Oak, mahogany, Spanish chestnut, and walnut may be fumed in this way.

2 *Potassium permanganate crystals* dissolved in water form a cheap brown stain which is often used to darken softwood flooring. This stain tends to fade in strong sunlight.

3 *Potassium bichromate* (poisonous) dissolved in water may be used to darken mahogany and similar timbers.

Fig. 226 gives a summary of information on stains.

### OUTSIDE WOODWORK

This needs a protective or preservative rather than a purely decorative finishing treatment because most timbers used for outside work will rot if left untreated (see Chapter 8).

Either (a) moisture must be kept away from the wood by putting a waterproof skin over the surface (paint, varnish, etc.), or (b) dry rot and similar fungi must be prevented from attacking the damp timber by the use of chemical preservatives (creosote or other commercial preparations).

The timber (fencing, gates, etc.) must be well soaked in the preservative (Fig. 227a and b). It is of little use just to brush on one thin coat as this is soon leached out by rain and snow.

Railway sleepers and telegraph poles are preserved by forcing creosote into them under pressure in large sealed tanks.

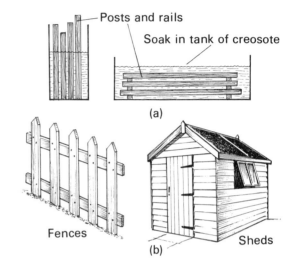

Several coats of preservative brushed on each year (preferably during summer when wood is relatively dry)

Fig. 227

# 8 Wood

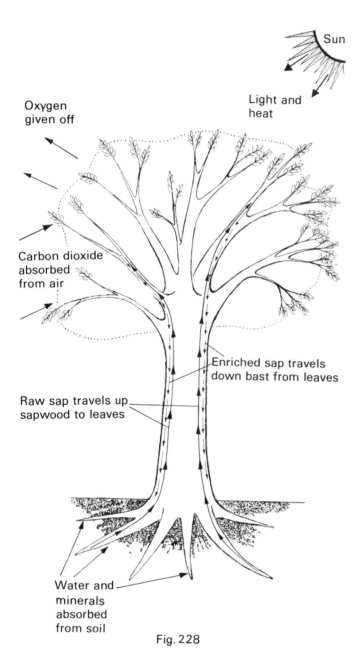

Oxygen given off

Light and heat

Sun

Carbon dioxide absorbed from air

Enriched sap travels down bast from leaves

Raw sap travels up sapwood to leaves

Water and minerals absorbed from soil

Fig. 228

Trees, like other plants, grow by absorbing carbon dioxide through their leaves, and water and mineral salts through their roots. As a result of the action of sunlight absorbed by chlorophyll (the green substance in leaves), these chemicals combine to form sugar, the tree's food. This sugar enriches the sap which has travelled up from the roots and is then carried away from the leaves to all parts of the tree (Fig. 228).

Fig. 229 shows a section cut along the grain through the centre of the tree (radial section), Fig. 230 shows a section cut nearer to one side of the trunk (tangential section), and Fig. 231 a cross section.

Each part of the tree while it is growing has a special job to do, and when the tree is cut down and seasoned (dried) for use, the structure (construction) of the tree will affect the way in which the timber can be used.

## STRUCTURE

**Bark** is a corky layer which protects the tree from the weather and insect attacks.

**Bast** (inner bark) carries enriched sap from the leaves down the branches and trunk to all the growing parts of the tree. As the outer layers of bast die off they become part of the bark.

**Growth rings** are formed by new layers of cells being produced by the cambium layer, a ring of dividing cells which also produces the bast or inner bark.

Because new growth rings are produced each year in most trees growing in cool countries (see map, Fig. 233), they have two parts. The quick spring growth produces a thick layer of rather soft wood because of the number of large wide tubes filled with rising sap. The slower summer growth produces a closer, harder and usually darker texture. Less sap is needed and so the tubes are narrower (Fig. 232a). During autumn and winter, active growth stops.

Tropical trees, such as mahogany, ebony and balsa, produce growth rings throughout the year as there is no winter season as we know it in the parts of the world where they grow. Thus there is little variation in the size of the tubes (Fig. 232b).

**Sapwood** is the name given to the newly-formed outer layer of growth rings. The 'raw' sap rises (from the roots) through these outer layers to the leaves. Sapwood is usually softer in texture and lighter in colour than heartwood. It should not be used for furniture-making or good class joinery as it is more likely to be attacked by insects and fungi than heartwood (see pages 95–6).

**Heartwood** is the centre part of the tree which is harder, stronger and often a richer colour than the sapwood.

**Medullary rays**, the 'figure' or 'silver rays' clearly seen in oak or beech, are groups of special cells which store the tree's food. They radiate from the centre of the tree rather like spokes of a wheel and are almost invisible in some timbers.

**Pith** is the tree's first growth as a seedling. It serves no purpose in the grown tree and shrivels away, leaving a spongy brown 'string' up the centre of the trunk.

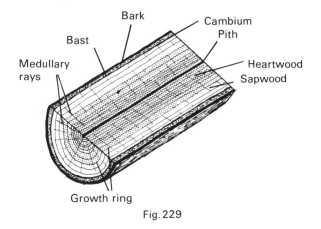

Fig. 229

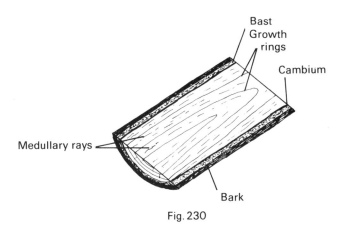

Fig. 230

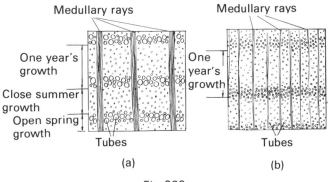

Fig. 232

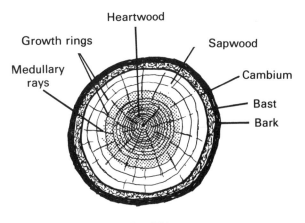

Fig. 231

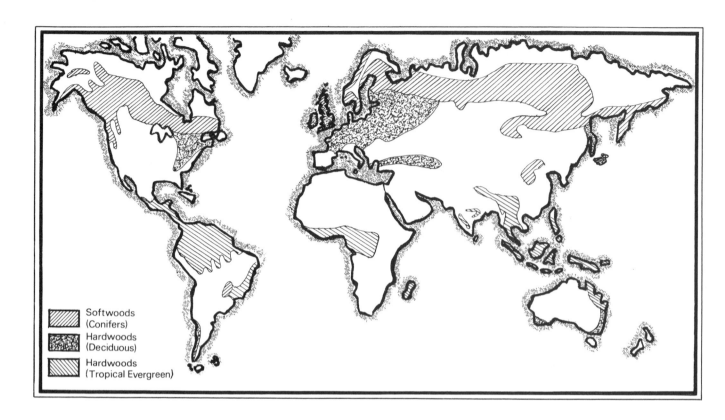

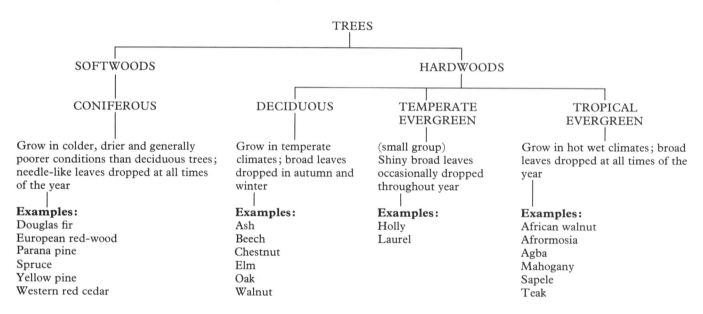

TREES

SOFTWOODS

HARDWOODS

CONIFEROUS

Grow in colder, drier and generally poorer conditions than deciduous trees; needle-like leaves dropped at all times of the year

**Examples:**
Douglas fir
European red-wood
Parana pine
Spruce
Yellow pine
Western red cedar

DECIDUOUS

Grow in temperate climates; broad leaves dropped in autumn and winter

**Examples:**
Ash
Beech
Chestnut
Elm
Oak
Walnut

TEMPERATE EVERGREEN

(small group)
Shiny broad leaves occasionally dropped throughout year

**Examples:**
Holly
Laurel

TROPICAL EVERGREEN

Grow in hot wet climates; broad leaves dropped at all times of the year

**Examples:**
African walnut
Afrormosia
Agba
Mahogany
Sapele
Teak

Fig. 233

## THE MAIN GROUPS OF TIMBERS

Timbers are classified into two main groups or types – softwoods and hardwoods (Fig. 233).

Fig. 233 also shows the main areas of the world where each type of tree grows; information about some of the common softwoods and hardwoods is given in Figs. 234, 235 and 236.

## SOURCES, CHARACTERISTICS AND USES OF COMMON SOFTWOODS

| TIMBER & ORIGIN | COLOUR | WEIGHT | GRAIN TYPE | WORKABILITY | USES | SPECIAL NOTES |
|---|---|---|---|---|---|---|
| **Douglas fir** (Oregon or British Columbian pine) West coast USA and Canada | Pale brown | Medium-light | Very even straight and almost knot-free | Quite good; splits easily when nailed | General joinery, plywood | Long wide 'clear' boards available |
| **European red wood** (Red deal, Scots pine) Europe, North and West Asia | Pale red-brown, sapwood pale fawn | Medium-light | Often knotty | Generally easy | General carpentry and joinery, packing cases, fencing | |
| **Parana pine** Brazil (South America) | Light to dark brown with red streaks; sapwood cream | Medium to medium heavy | Close, even, sometimes brittle; growth rings indistinct | Generally good | Interior joinery and fittings | 300 mm wide boards available; sometimes warps and twists badly |
| **Spruce** (White deal, White fir) North America, North Europe | Whitish with fine brown lines | Fairly light | Even spring and summer growth rings | Generally good; takes screws, nails and glues well | Interior joinery, food boxes (oars and masts: use Sitka spruce only) | No smell, not durable |
| **Yellow pine** (Quebec pine) Eastern USA and Canada | Pale yellow | Light | Very fine smooth grain | Excellent; glues, nails and screws very easily | Pattern making (for casting); high class joinery | Very stable |
| **Western red cedar** West coast USA and Canada | Fawn to red-brown; weathers to silver grey | Light | Soft straight grained | Easy, but end grain tends to crumble | Outside cladding, sheds and green-houses | Naturally resistant to rot and beetles |

Fig. 234

## SOURCES, CHARACTERISTICS AND USES OF COMMON DECIDUOUS HARDWOODS

| TIMBER & ORIGIN | COLOUR | WEIGHT | GRAIN TYPE | WORKABILITY | USES | SPECIAL NOTES |
|---|---|---|---|---|---|---|
| **Ash** Northern Europe, North America | Whitish with pale brown lines | Medium | Coarse, straight | Fairly easy | Tool handles, sports equipment, vehicle framework | Very elastic and shock resistant; can be steamed to shape |
| **Beech** Europe, Japan | Pale brown, golden fleck (medullary rays) | Medium-heavy | Hard, very smooth and close | Works well with sharp tools | Wooden tools, turnery, furniture, plywood | Very stable; can be steamed to shape |
| **Chestnut** (Sweet or Spanish) Europe | Pale straw | Medium | Coarse, usually straight | Fairly easy, splits easily | Fencing, turnery, furniture | Rather like 'plain sawn' oak |
| **Elm** Northern Europe, North America | Pale to dark brown, sometimes has purple tinge | Medium-light | Coarse, sometimes very twisty | Fairly easy unless twisty grained | Decorative panelling, furniture, coffins | Withstands splitting, rot resistant |
| **Oak** Europe, North America, Japan | Deep straw 'silver figure' | Heavy | Hard, coarse, sometimes knotty | Medium to difficult (Japanese usually easier) | Furniture, building, decorative panelling, fencing | Weather and rot resistant if sapwood cut out |
| **Walnut** Europe, North America | Grey-brown to chocolate-brown, very attractive markings | Medium-heavy | Hard, very smooth and close | Works well with sharp tools | Furniture, veneers | Scarce, 'burr' veneers very decorative |

Fig. 235

SOURCES, CHARACTERISTICS AND USES OF COMMON TROPICAL EVERGREEN HARDWOODS

| TIMBER & ORIGIN | COLOUR | WEIGHT | GRAIN TYPE | WORKABILITY | USES | SPECIAL NOTES |
|---|---|---|---|---|---|---|
| **African walnut** (Nigerian walnut) West Africa | Golden brown with black streaks | Medium | Interlocking 'stripe' effect, fairly fine | Fairly easy, but sharp tools needed | Furniture, panelling, veneers | |
| **Afrormosia** West Africa | Brown with darker streaks | Fairly heavy | Fine with interlocking grain, hard | Quite good | Furniture, flooring, ship fittings | Often used as substitute for teak |
| **Agba** West Africa | Yellowish-pink to pale reddish-brown | Medium–light | Fine and fairly hard | Easy; nails, screws and glues well | Joinery and inside fittings, plywood, flooring | Large sizes available free of defects |
| **Mahogany** West Africa, West Indies, Central America | Pink-brown to deep red-brown | Medium | Often interlocking (African coarser than other types) | Fairly easy, except for interlocking grain | Furniture, ship, railway and inside fittings, veneers, pattern making | |
| **Sapele** West and Central Africa | Rich red-brown | Medium–heavy | Often interlocking, fine to medium texture, sometimes hard | Medium, sometimes difficult if interlocking grain | Furniture, veneers and panelling, inside fittings, flooring | Fairly resistant to rot and insect attack |
| **Teak** Burma, India, Malaysia | Rich brown | Medium–heavy | Coarse, 'oily', hard | Quite good with sharp tools | Laboratory benches, outside furniture, constructional work, veneers, panelling, ship work | Very stable, rot and insect resistant, rather scarce |

Fig. 236

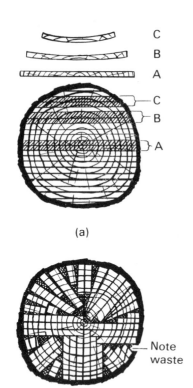

(a)

Fig. 237                (b)

Contracts as wood
looses water (becomes
lighter) during seasoning,
thus raising the wood

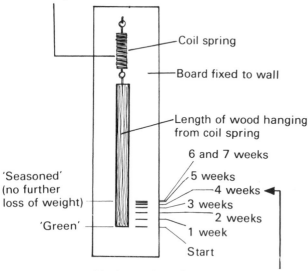

— Coil spring

— Board fixed to wall

— Length of wood hanging
from coil spring

6 and 7 weeks

5 weeks

4 weeks

3 weeks

2 weeks

1 week

Start

'Seasoned'
(no further
loss of weight)

'Green'

Mark position of bottom end of wood
each week until no further upward
movement takes place

Fig. 238

## CONVERSION

After felling (cutting down), trees are converted –
that is, sawn into planks, boards or 'squares' of
several sizes. Fig. 237a and b shows the two main
ways of doing this.

**Plain or slash sawn** is the quicker, easier and
cheaper method. Very little wood is wasted, but all
the boards except for middle cut boards (A) will
warp (bow outwards at the edges) when the wood
dries out. Boards cut from nearer the middle of the
tree (B) warp less than those cut at C.

**Quarter or rift sawn** is a method of conversion
which gives more boards which do not warp. Also,
as the medullary rays run parallel to the sides of the
board, figured timber is obtained (e.g. 'figured' oak
or 'fiddle-back' mahogany). This is often more
decorative than plain sawn timber.

Quarter sawing is more wasteful than plain
sawing, but does provide wide boards for table tops
and so on which are warp free.

## SEASONING

When felled, a tree contains a great deal of water in
the form of sap, especially if cut down in spring or
summer when it is in active growth. This 'green'
timber needs to be seasoned (dried) before it can be
used for most woodworking jobs, because as it dries,
wood always shrinks, sometimes changes shape
(warps and twists), and occasionally develops
'shakes' (splits). The amount of water in a piece of
wood is called its moisture content and this is
written as a percentage of the dry weight of the
wood. Thus, freshly felled timber might have a
moisture content (m/c) of 90%, the weight of the
water in the wood being nearly equal to the weight
of the wood when dried out. Seasoned wood will
have a moisture content (m/c) of between 10%
and 20%.

Fig. 238 shows how you can dry a piece of 'green'
timber in a warm dry room and observe the change
in weight as it dries out.

## Method of seasoning

There are two basic methods of seasoning timber.

### (a) Natural (air) seasoning

Green timber is stacked as in Fig. 239 so that air can circulate freely round each board. 'Stickers' (stacking sticks of seasoned softwood) support the boards and allow an air space between each one. The stickers are placed one above the other to prevent the boards sagging or twisting. Timber 'in stick' should be protected from fierce overhead sun, and snow and rain.

Wood, because it contains many tubes (see Fig. 232), may be likened to a bundle of drinking straws. Any moisture in the tubes will evaporate quicker from their open ends than through their sides. Thus the ends of boards tend to dry out and shrink faster than the rest. This often causes splitting of the board ends. It may be prevented by sealing the end grain either with a thick coat of paint or with a wooden cleat nailed on as in Fig. 240.

The length of time needed for natural seasoning of timber depends mainly upon the moisture content of the green timber when stacked, and the thickness of the boards.

Usually one year is allowed per 25 mm of board thickness: e.g. for 25 mm board, one year, for 50 mm board, two years, and so on.

### (b) Kiln seasoning

Kiln seasoning is a way of speeding up the natural seasoning process by blowing warm air round and between the 'sticked' boards.

The wood is stacked on a trolley which is run in to the kiln, a specially designed building like a large brick shed, where air is circulated by electric fans (Fig. 241). Steam is blown into the kiln through jet holes in a pipe which runs along the kiln walls. This makes the air humid and stops the wood from drying out too quickly. The temperature of the air in the kiln is raised to about 40°C and the moisture gradually reduced so that after a few weeks the timber is fully seasoned. By controlling both the temperature and humidity (moisture in the air) the timber may be seasoned to the degree of m/c needed for any particular job. For indoor work, wood is kiln seasoned to a m/c of between 10% and 14%.

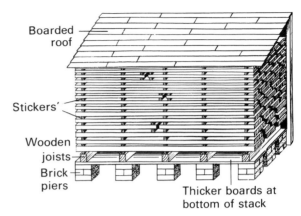

Boarded roof

Stickers'

Wooden joists

Brick piers

Thicker boards at bottom of stack

Fig. 239

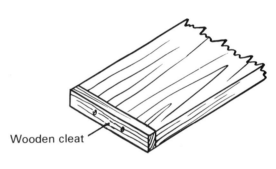

Wooden cleat

Fig. 240

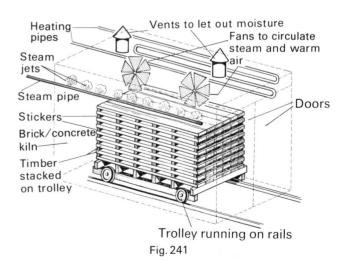

Heating pipes

Vents to let out moisture

Fans to circulate steam and warm air

Steam jets

Steam pipe

Doors

Stickers

Brick/concrete kiln

Timber stacked on trolley

Trolley running on rails

Fig. 241

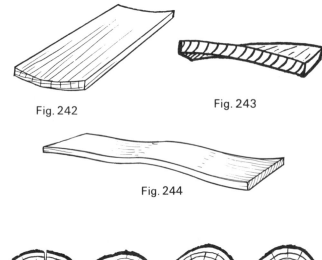

Fig. 242

Fig. 243

Fig. 244

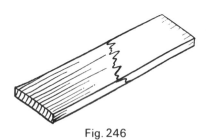

| Radial | Heart | Star | Cup |
|--------|-------|------|-----|
| (a) | (b) | (c) | (d) |

Fig. 245

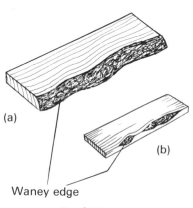

Fig. 246

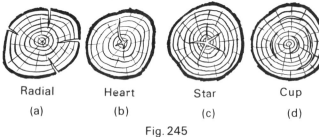

(a)

(b)

Waney edge

Fig. 247

## TIMBER FAULTS

Some of the faults or defects often found in timber are shown in Figs. 242 to 247.

**Warping** (Figs. 242 and 237a) is hollowing or cupping *across* the board. On narrow boards or laths this is not very important, but it would be a serious fault in a table top. Timber which is quarter sawn is free from this defect which develops during seasoning.

**Wind (Twist)** (Fig. 243). Timber which is 'in wind' or 'in winding' is difficult to plane true. Wood is tested for twist by means of winding strips (see Fig. 55b).

**Bowing** (Fig. 244), where a board sags in the middle or at intervals *along* its length, often happens when too few 'stickers' are used to support it during seasoning.

**Shakes** (Fig. 245a to d) are splits which usually develop along the grain while the timber is being seasoned. They are most often found at the ends of boards or logs, and are caused by uneven drying out of the timber (see page 93 and Fig. 240).

**Upsets** (Fig. 246) are shakes or jagged splits which run across the grain. They are probably caused by severe jarring of the tree during felling and are mostly seen in tropical timbers.

**Waney edge** (Fig. 247a and b) is the name given to the untrimmed ege of a board as cut from the tree (Fig. 247a). If this outer edge (which sometimes retains the bark) is not all sawn off, faulty square-edged boards are produced as in Fig. 247b.

**Knots** (Fig. 248a and b). A knot is seen as a cross section of a branch (see Fig. 231) where it starts to grow out of the trunk or out of a larger branch of the tree.

Large knots seriously weaken timber and, because they distort the grain of wood around them, most knots spoil the appearance of otherwise clear boards. Knots often cause difficulty in planing, the grain around them tending to tear as the plane passes over it.

**Staining** Wood may become discoloured or stained for various reasons. For example, so-called 'brown' oak is cut from trees which have been attacked by an otherwise harmless fungus which causes the wood to turn a warm shade of brown. The sapwood of softwoods sometimes turns slightly blue during seasoning, and this too is caused by a harmless fungoid attack.

Where oak and certain other hardwoods are in contact with iron, the acid in the timber attacks the iron, corroding it and causing the timber around it to turn black.

## DAMAGE TO WOOD

### Wood boring beetles

Woodworms, as they are often called, are the larvae (grubs) of wood-boring beetles and cause a great deal of damage to furniture and building timbers. The *Furniture beetle*, *Lyctus beetle*, and *Death Watch beetle* are the most common in this country. The life cycle of these beetles falls into the same four stages as the butterfly.

Stage 1 *Egg*: laid by female beetle in cracks or crevices in the wood during the summer months (Fig. 249a). After a few weeks the egg hatches into a larva.

Stage 2 *Larva*: the 'worm' or grub eats its way into the wood for one to ten years according to the type of beetle (Fig. 249b). During this time much damage may be done; a severe attack will end in the collapse of the wood.

Stage 3 *Pupa*: the larva changes into a pupa, or chrysalis near the surface of the wood (Fig. 249c). The pupal stage lasts about a month or so, and during this period the larva develops into a beetle.

Stage 4 *The adult beetle* emerges from small holes (1 mm to 3 mm in diameter) and flies off to mate (Fig. 249d). This adult stage is a very short one.

The Furniture beetle, as its name suggests, attacks interior woodwork, as does the Lyctus beetle which also causes damage to the sapwood of oak and other hardwoods during air seasoning. For this reason sapwood should not be used for furniture making. The Death Watch beetle is larger than the

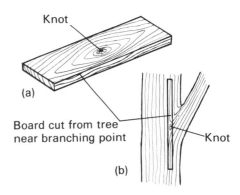

Fig. 248

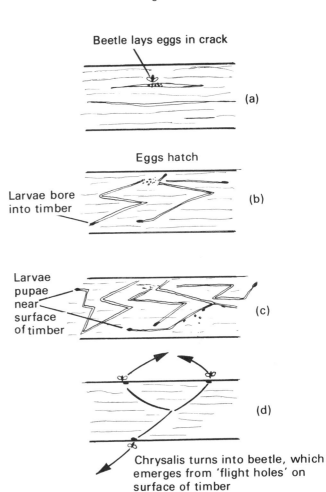

Fig. 249

other two and attacks beams and other main timbers in old buildings, especially if the wood is slightly damp. The wood in many cathedrals and church roofs has been severely damaged by this beetle.

### Treatment

Small 'flight' holes just over 1 mm across and from which fine wood dust can often be shaken are a sure sign of woodworm in furniture. If there are only a few worm holes in the surface of the wood, chemical insecticides can be injected into them and brushed well into the surrounding wood. Badly infected wood should be cut out, burnt and replaced.

As a safety precaution the underneath of chairs, the backs of drawers, and so on should be inspected each summer so that any attack can be discovered before too much damage has been done.

### Dry rot

Dry rot is caused by a type of fungus which attacks damp timber. Affected timber turns brown, becomes light in weight, and develops cracks along and across the grain. Badly infected timber may be so seriously weakened by dry rot fungus that it can be crumbled in the hand.

An attack of dry rot occurs in this way.

Stage 1  The spores (seeds), each one of which is too small to be seen without a microscope, are blown about in the air or carried on the feet of insects, birds, or animals. When spores come to rest on a piece of damp wood they start to grow, sending out fine hair-like rootlets which bore into the wood (Fig. 250a).

Stage 2  These rootlets branch out and spread right through the timber (Fig. 250b).

Stage 3  Fruit bodies, somewhat like stemless orange-brown toadstools, form on the surface of the wood. When these ripen they shoot out millions of spores into the air, and the process is repeated (Fig. 250c).

### Prevention

To prevent dry rot attack, timber must either be kept dry or be treated with a preservative (see Chapter 7). Once outside paintwork starts to crack

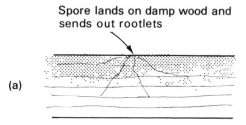

(a) Spore lands on damp wood and sends out rootlets

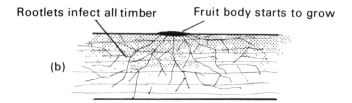

(b) Rootlets infect all timber    Fruit body starts to grow

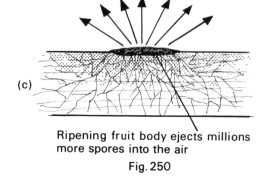

(c) Ripening fruit body ejects millions more spores into the air

Fig. 250

or peel, moisture gets into the wood and so, sooner or later, does dry rot.

### Testing for dry rot

Very often dry rot does not appear at the surface of the wood, especially when this has been painted, but if it is suspected, push in a thin-bladed knife. If the blade passes easily into the wood it is almost certainly rotten. Sometimes a musty smell may also be noticed.

### Treatment

Step 1 Cut away the infected wood and all timber within at least a foot of it.

Step 2 Carefully brush up all wood dust and dirt and burn this along with the infected wood which has been cut out – it is likely to contain millions of spores.

Step 3 Find the cause of the damp and cure it. Failure to do this will result in a further attack of dry rot.

Step 4 Treat all nearby surfaces (including brickwork) with a suitable preservative and apply plenty of preservative to all new wood before fitting it in place of the infected timber.

## MANUFACTURED 'MAN-MADE' BOARDS

### Veneers

Veneers (thin sheets of wood cut from 0·5 mm to 3 mm thick) are used either to make plywood, laminboard, blockboard, etc., or to decorate plainer timbers (see Chapter 4).

Veneers for making plywood are *rotary cut* (peeled).

Logs are first soaked in nearly boiling water, or steamed to soften the fibres (Fig. 251a), and then the bark is removed.

Next, a steamed log about 2 m long is mounted on a machine like a large lathe. In place of a turning chisel, a knife the full length of the log peels off a continuous sheet of veneer (Fig. 251b) as if it were unwinding a Swiss roll.

Finally, this long sheet of veneer is cut into lengths and dried (Fig. 251c).

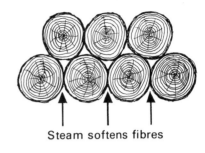

Steam softens fibres

(a)

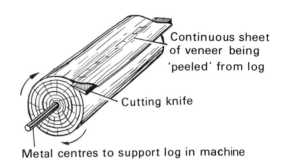

Continuous sheet of veneer being 'peeled' from log

Cutting knife

Metal centres to support log in machine

(b)

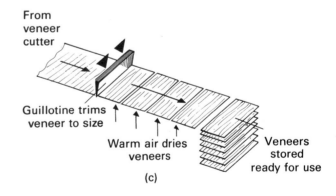

From veneer cutter

Guillotine trims veneer to size

Warm air dries veneers

Veneers stored ready for use

(c)

Fig. 251

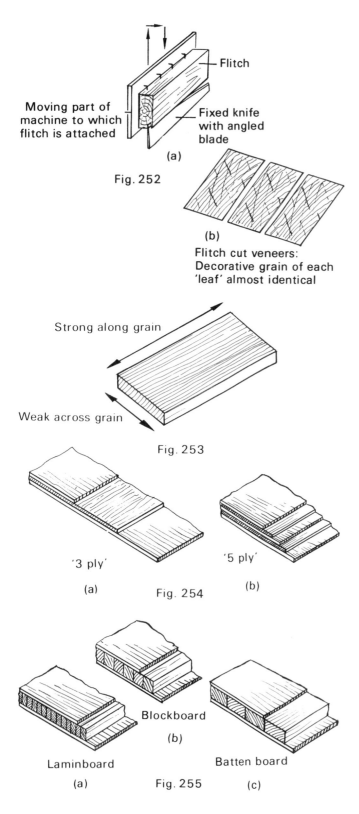

Moving part of machine to which flitch is attached

Flitch

Fixed knife with angled blade

(a)

Fig. 252

(b)

Flitch cut veneers: Decorative grain of each 'leaf' almost identical

Strong along grain

Weak across grain

Fig. 253

'3 ply'

(a)

Fig. 254

'5 ply'

(b)

Laminboard

(a)

Blockboard

(b)

Batten board

(c)

Fig. 255

Decorative veneers are usually *flitch cut* (sliced). A flitch – a quarter sawn slab of attractively grained wood – is steamed and mounted as in Fig. 252a. A long cutter blade shaped like a guillotine slices off thin sheets of veneer. In this way 'matched' veneers are obtained which are more highly figured than those which are rotary cut (Fig. 252b).

## Plywood

Wood is strong along the grain but fairly weak across it (Fig. 253). Wide boards free from knots and other faults are difficult to obtain, and they 'move' (shrink or swell across the grain) in very dry or damp conditions.

Plywood is largely free from all these faults. It is made with each veneer or 'ply' glued with its grain running at right angles to the veneers on either side of it (Fig. 254a and b). This gives the board great strength combined with lightness. Note that an odd number of plies (3, 5, 7, etc.) is always used so that the grain on both sides of the plywood runs in the same direction.

Much plywood is made using synthetic resin glues (see Chapter 3, pages 54–5). This gives a completely waterproof board which can be used for outside work and for boat-building (see Chapter 12, pages 147–8).

Curved shapes can be made using jigs as in Fig. 116, and thin plywood can be steamed and moulded to shape in a similar way (see Chapter 3, pages 41–3).

## Built-up boards

If a board over 16 mm thick is wanted, the centre plies are replaced by a 'core' of straight grained softwood strips, glued with their grain at right angles to the thick outer plies.

**Laminboard** (Fig. 255a) uses very narrow strips, often about 3 mm wide. This produces a particularly stable board.

**Blockboard** (Fig. 255b) has core strips about 20 mm wide. This gives a cheaper board which is strong and virtually warp free.

**Battenboard** (Fig. 255c), in which the core strips

are up to 75 mm wide, is used where a very thick built-up board is needed. It is not quite so stable as laminboard or blockboard.

Birch, beech, gaboon and Douglas fir are commonly used for making plywood and built-up boards. If a decorative grain is required, as when making furniture, the boards may be faced with oak, mahogany or other attractively grained veneers.

Built-up boards cannot readily be jointed in the same ways as solid timber. Fig. 256a to d shows some of the usual methods of corner jointing them.

The edges of the boards are unsightly and may chip easily. They are therefore lipped (see Figs. 59 and 257a to e).

**Chipboard** (usually 13 mm to 22 mm thick) is made from compressed wood shavings mixed with synthetic resin glue (Fig. 258). The pressed chipboard is machine sanded – as are all built-up boards – before being sent out from the factory.

Chipboard may be used plain or with a paper surface to give a better finish when painted. It may also be obtained ready veneered or with hard, patterned plastics surfaces. Jointing and lipping is carried out as in Figs. 256 and 257.

**Hardboard** is made from pulped wood, mixed with adhesive and pressed into sheets 3 mm to 6 mm thick by passing between heavy heated rollers (Fig. 259).

Patterned or moulded hardboard or pegboard (perforated hardboard) (Fig. 260a to d) is made by using specially contoured rollers during manufacture. Exterior grade is a specially waterproofed type of hardboard. As with chipboard, plastics or veneer surfaced varieties are manufactured, suitable for panelling or sliding doors (see Figs. 132 and 134). The edges of 'standard' grade hardboard should be protected as the fibres are easily frayed out.

**Plastics sheet**
Laminated plastics sheet of the 'Formica' type is manufactured from sheets of paper bonded with special synthetic resins, under great pressure and heat. Many patterns, including 'wood grains' with or without textured finishes, are available in sheets about 1·5 mm thick.

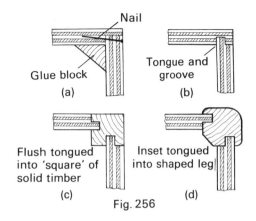

Fig. 256

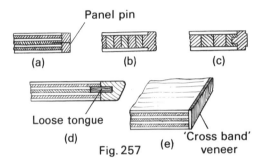

Fig. 257

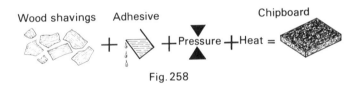

Fig. 258

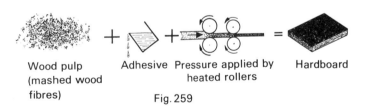

Fig. 259

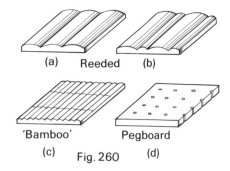

(a)    Reeded    (b)

'Bamboo'    Pegboard
(c)    Fig. 260    (d)

## Cutting

To cut laminated plastics sheet do *not* use a tenon saw as the hard material will blunt the teeth. Instead use a hacksaw blade gripped in a padsaw handle. Always cut plastics sheet 3 mm oversize to allow for trimming the edges after gluing to a board.

## Sticking

There are two ways to stick plastics sheet to plywood or other board: (a) using a synthetic resin glue if a veneer press or similar method of cramping large enough to take the work is available (e.g. table top). The back of the laminate and the top surface of the plywood should be coated with synthetic resin glue and firmly and evenly pressed together until completely set.

NOTE: *put a sheet of polythene or thick paper each side of the work to prevent surplus glue sticking it to the press (Fig. 261).*

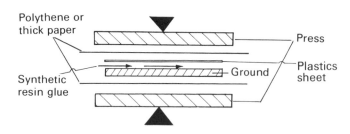

Polythene or thick paper

Synthetic resin glue

Press

Plastics sheet

Ground

Fig. 261

(b) using an impact (contact) adhesive – but be sure that the plastics sheet is stuck down in *exactly* the correct position. Remember that once the glued surfaces touch they stick together instantly and no adjustment in positioning is possible.

To overcome this difficulty, push two drawing pins firmly into one long edge of the board so that the edge of the plastics sheet can first be 'offered up' to the underside of the pin heads. This will ensure that the edge of the plastics sheet is parallel to the edge of the board *before* the sheet is lowered on to it (Fig. 262).

Spread an even coat of adhesive on both joining surfaces and leave to dry for about 15 minutes.

Offer up one long edge to the pins, then carefully lower the plastics sheet on to the plywood. Press firmly down, first applying pressure at the centre to avoid trapping bubbles of air.

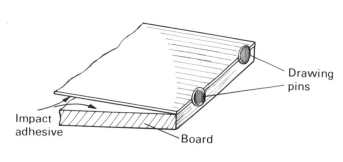

Drawing pins

Impact adhesive

Board

Fig. 262

Once the plastics sheet has been pressed well down on to the plywood, its edges can be trimmed. A smoothing plane can be used for this, but the blade will quickly become blunted; an alternative is to use a smooth file followed by emery cloth or glasspaper wrapped round a block of wood. Plastics lipping glued round the edges of the board will hide the edge of both the plastics sheet and the plywood (Fig. 263a and b).

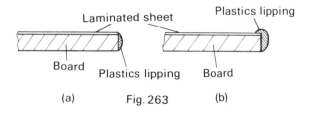

Laminated sheet    Plastics lipping

Board
Plastics lipping    Board

(a)    Fig. 263    (b)

# 9 Tools

## PRELIMINARY NOTES

The purpose of this chapter is to help the reader easily and quickly to identify common woodworking tools and pieces of small workshop equipment, and to give basic information on their construction, maintenance, and use. Cross references are given where tool uses are described elsewhere in this book.

To find out facts quickly about any woodworking tool:

(a) decide what type of a tool it is (for instance, a marking-out tool, a sharp edged tool, a cramping tool, etc.);

(b) look up the tool under that general heading in the table below. This will give you the page reference and the number of the drawing which illustrates the tool.

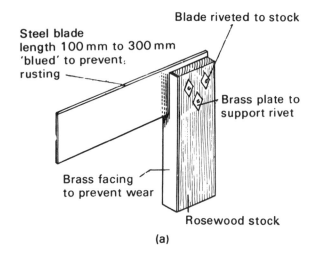

Steel blade
length 100 mm to 300 mm
'blued' to prevent
rusting

Blade riveted to stock

Brass plate to
support rivet

Brass facing
to prevent wear

Rosewood stock

(a)

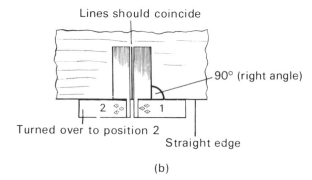

Lines should coincide

90° (right angle)

2

1

Turned over to position 2

Straight edge

(b)

Fig. 264

## Boring tools
Bits: centre p. 116, Fig. 312
　　　*expanding* p. 116, Fig. 314
　　　*improved (screw centre)* p. 116, Fig. 313
Bits: twist
　　　*countersink* p. 117, Fig. 318
　　　*Forstner* p. 117, Fig. 317
　　　*Irwin* p. 117, Fig. 315
　　　*Jennings* p. 117, Fig. 316
　　　*solid centre* p. 117, Fig. 315
Bradawl p. 117, Fig. 319
Carpenter's brace p. 116, Fig. 309
Twist drill p. 116, Fig. 311
Wheel brace p. 116, Fig. 310

## Work-holding equipment
Bench hook (sawing board) p. 118, Fig. 320
Cradle p. 118, Fig. 323
Cramps (clamps): *bench holdfast* p. 120, Fig. 329
　　　　　　　　*F* p. 119, Fig. 327
　　　　　　　　*G* p. 119, Fig. 325
　　　　　　　　*handscrew* p. 119, Fig. 328
　　　　　　　　*rack* p. 119, Fig. 326
　　　　　　　　*sash* p. 119, Fig. 324
Mitre box (block) p. 118, Fig. 321
Shooting board p. 118, Fig. 322

## Miscellaneous tools
Files and rasps p. 122, Fig. 337
　Surform rasp p. 122, Fig. 338
Hammers:
　　　　　*claw* p. 121, Fig. 333
　　　　　*pin* p. 120, Fig. 332
　　　　　*warrington* p. 120, Fig. 331
Mallets:
　　　　　*woodworker's* p. 121, Fig. 334
　　　　　*carvers'* p. 190, Fig. 66
Pincers p. 121, Fig. 335
Scraper p. 122, Fig. 336
Scratch stock p. 122, Figs. 170a and 184
Screwdriver p. 120, Fig. 330

# TOOLS FOR MARKING OUT AND TESTING

## Try square (Fig. 264)
**Uses** Setting out lines at right angles to a side or edge (Figs. 3e, 79b, 80a). Testing for 'squareness' (Figs. 3b, 3j, 22b, 41b, 264b).

## Testing a try square for accuracy
Step 1 Hold the square against a true edge (Fig. 264b, position 1).

Step 2 Mark off a line along the edge of the blade.

Step 3 Turn the square over to position 2 and mark off another line. This will coincide with the first line if the square is 'true'.

## Mitre square (Fig. 265)
**Use** Setting out and checking angles of 45° and 135°, as in making a picture frame joint (Fig. 265b).

## Adjustable bevel (Fig. 266)
**Use** Setting out and checking angled work (e.g. angled bridle joint (Fig. 17d); angled mortice and tenon joint (Fig. 65c and f)).

## Marking knives (Fig. 267)
The blade should be ground to a fine knife edge so that it will fit close up against the edge of the try square blade.

**Uses** Setting out shoulder lines, etc. (Fig. 79b). The marking knife gives greater accuracy than a pencil line.

## Marking gauge (Fig. 268)
**Use** Gauging lines parallel to an edge or side *along* the grain of wood, usually when planing to size (Figs. 3c, 14a).

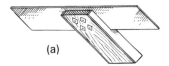

(a)

Construction similiar to that of the try square

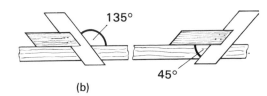

135°

45°

(b)

Fig. 265

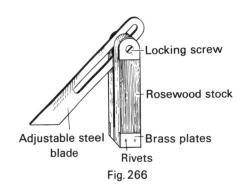

Locking screw

Rosewood stock

Brass plates

Adjustable steel blade

Rivets

Fig. 266

(a) All steel

(b) Wooden handle

Fig. 267

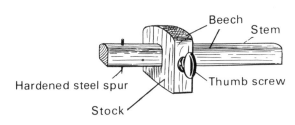

Beech

Stem

Hardened steel spur

Thumb screw

Stock

Fig. 268

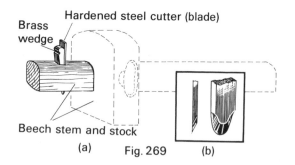

Brass wedge

Hardened steel cutter (blade)

Beech stem and stock

(a)  Fig. 269  (b)

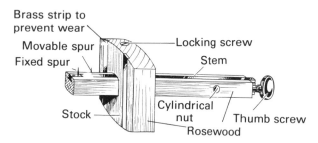

Brass strip to prevent wear

Movable spur

Fixed spur

Locking screw

Stem

Stock

Cylindrical nut

Thumb screw

Rosewood

Fig. 270

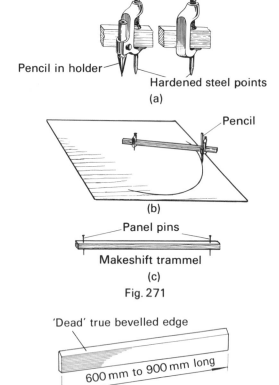

Pencil in holder

Hardened steel points

(a)

Pencil

(b)

Panel pins

Makeshift trammel

(c)

Fig. 271

'Dead' true bevelled edge

600 mm to 900 mm long

Fig. 272

## Cutting gauge (Fig. 269)

Made like a marking gauge, but with a cutting-blade in place of the spur (Fig. 269b). Note that the blade is ground and sharpened from one side only.

**Uses** Gauging lines *across* the grain of wood.

Setting out shoulders of lap dovetails (Fig. 34a).

Trimming edges of veneers before cross banding (Fig. 164a).

Cutting small rebates for inlay lines (Fig. 165).

## Mortice gauge (Fig. 270)

This has one fixed and one adjustable spur so that it can be set to the width of a mortice chisel (Fig. 21b). (Instructions for setting are given on page 10.)

**Use** Setting out mortice and tenon and bridle joints (Figs. 16, 21a, 24a).

## Trammel (Fig. 271)

**Use** The 'heads' are cramped to a convenient strip of wood, and used (a) as compasses to draw large circles (using a pencil in the holder), as in Fig. 271b; (b) as large dividers when setting out shaped work (using the points only).

## Straight edge (Fig. 272)

**Uses** Testing long lengths (or widths) for accuracy. Planing to size (Fig. 3a and b).

Edge jointing (Fig. 37a, b and c).

## Winding strips (Fig. 273)

These are made in pairs from straight grained hardwood with their edges true and parallel.

**Use** To check prepared timber for 'wind'. If wood is 'in winding', the top edges of the strips will not be parallel (Fig. 273b).

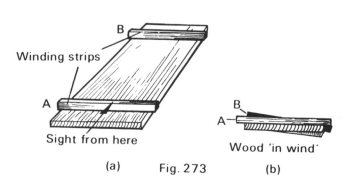

Winding strips

B

A

Sight from here

(a)  Fig. 273  (b)

Wood 'in wind'

B

A

# SAWS

## Rip saw (Fig. 274a)

**Use** Rough sawing *along* the grain (Fig. 274f).

*Blade* The blade is fixed to the handle with 'saw screws', a special type of nut and bolt (Fig. 274b). Saw blades should be lightly oiled when not in use.

*Teeth* Rip saw teeth are set (bent) alternately left and right to give clearance – that is, to prevent the sides of the blade binding in the saw cut or kerf (Fig. 274c). The teeth are filed square across the blade (Fig. 274d) with their front edges at right angles to the bottom edge of the blade (Fig. 274e). As a result they cut like a series of narrow chisels.

## Cross cut saw

**Use** Rough sawing *across* the grain. The blade and handle are similar to those of a rip saw, but the teeth are different. (Try using a rip saw to cut *across* the grain of a piece of scrapwood, and note how badly it tears the fibres.)

*Teeth* The teeth of a cross cut saw must be smaller than those of a rip saw, 3 mm to 5 mm pitch, and shaped as in Fig. 275a, b and c.

NOTE: *the outer knife edge of each tooth which slices the fibres before the front of the tooth chisels out the waste.*

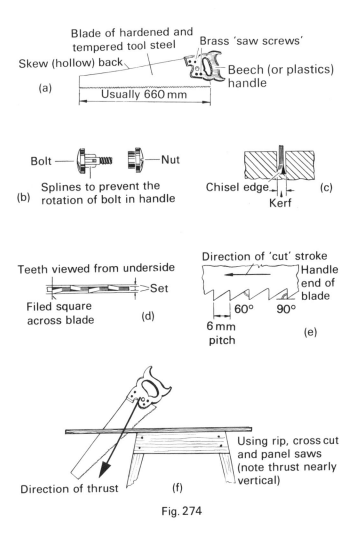

Fig. 274

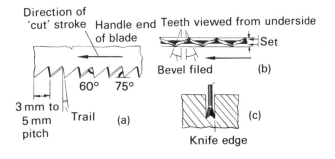

Fig. 275

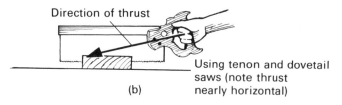

Blade (folded strip of brass or steel to stiffen thin steel blade)

'Cross cut' type teeth
Pitch 1.4 mm to 2.1 mm

200 mm to 350 mm

(a)

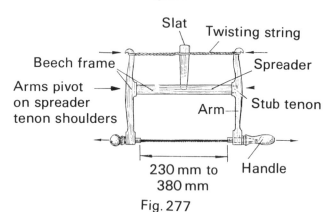

Direction of thrust

Using tenon and dovetail saws (note thrust nearly horizontal)

(b)

Fig. 276

Slat
Twisting string

Beech frame

Spreader

Arms pivot on spreader tenon shoulders

Arm

Stub tenon

230 mm to 380 mm

Handle

Fig. 277

## Panel saw

**Use** Sawing plywood, hardboard, etc., to size. This is a small cross cut saw having teeth of 3 mm pitch.

## Tenon saw (back saw) (Fig. 276)

**Uses** Accurate cutting to length across the grain (Fig. 3f). Cutting joints, e.g. tenons (Figs. 16d, e and f, 19b, 24g).

A folded strip (back) of brass or steel clamped over the top edge of the thin blade prevents it from buckling or twisting in use.

## Bow saw (Fig. 277)

**Use** Cutting curves (Fig. 103a), e.g. a circular table top. The narrow blade is tensioned (tightened) by twisting the string with the slat. The blade may be turned to cut at any angle by twisting *both* handles. Fig. 103b shows how the blade is held (and turned) in the frame.

## Coping saw (Fig. 278)

**Uses** Cutting waste from joints (Fig. 32g).

Cutting inside and outside curves in plywood, etc. (Fig. 103b). (Generally used for lighter and more accurate work than the bow saw.) Fig. 278b shows the method of fitting, tensioning and turning the blade.

NOTE: *do NOT apply heavy pressure when using a coping saw as the blade is brittle and breaks easily.*

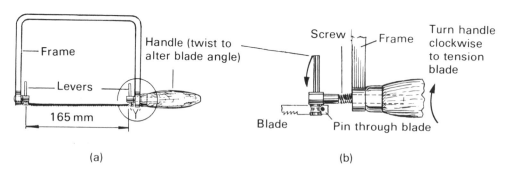

Frame

Handle (twist to alter blade angle)

Screw

Frame

Turn handle clockwise to tension blade

Levers

165 mm

Blade

Pin through blade

(a)

(b)

Fig. 278

**Fret saw** (Fig. 279)
**Use** Cutting very complex curves and shapes (inside and outside) in plywood or thick veneers. Fig. 279b shows how the blade is fitted. Note in Fig. 279c how thin work is supported when using a fret saw.

Fret saw blades are even finer than coping saw blades, so be careful!

**Compass saw** (Fig. 280)
**Uses** Cutting where there is not enough space to use a cross cut or rip saw.

Cutting curves or large holes well away from the edge of a board where a bow or coping saw cannot be used. (The short blade version (keyhole saw) is used for sawing down narrow slots.)

**Pad saw** (Fig. 281)
**Use** Where a compass saw is too large to use for cutting in confined spaces, holes, etc. (Fig. 104).

NOTE: *the blade (Fig. 281b) is slid into the handle when not in use, and locked in position with the two screws when required.*

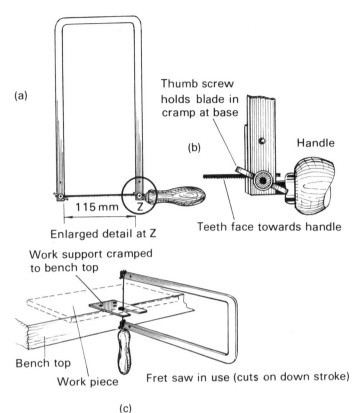

(a)

Thumb screw holds blade in cramp at base

(b)

Handle

115 mm

Teeth face towards handle

Enlarged detail at Z

Work support cramped to bench top

Bench top

Work piece

Fret saw in use (cuts on down stroke)

(c)

Fig. 279

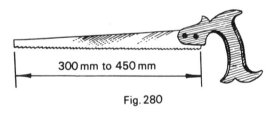

300 mm to 450 mm

Fig. 280

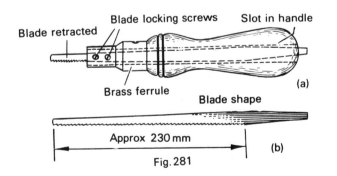

Blade retracted

Blade locking screws

Slot in handle

Brass ferrule

Blade shape

(a)

Approx 230 mm

(b)

Fig. 281

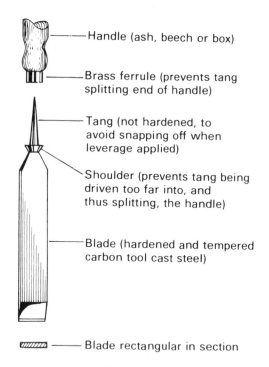

Handle (ash, beech or box)

Brass ferrule (prevents tang splitting end of handle)

Tang (not hardened, to avoid snapping off when leverage applied)

Shoulder (prevents tang being driven too far into, and thus splitting, the handle)

Blade (hardened and tempered carbon tool cast steel)

Blade rectangular in section

Fig. 282

## CHISELS AND GOUGES

**Firmer chisel** (Fig. 282)

**Uses** General benchwork and joint cutting (Figs. 14, 19a, 139).

NOTE: *do NOT strike chisel or gouge handle with a hammer as this will either split or severely damage them. Always use a mallet.*

SAFETY NOTE: *chisels, unless handled and stored with care, are soon damaged. Because they are sharp they can easily cause injury if not correctly held (see page 1).*

**Bevelled edge chisel** (Fig. 283)

**Uses** Cutting into corners, acute angles such as dovetails, etc. (Figs. 283b, 34d, e, f).

NOTE: *do NOT use this chisel for heavy work, as the blade is weaker than that of a firmer chisel.*

**Mortice chisels** (Fig. 284)

**Uses** Cutting mortices and any heavy work needing much leverage (Fig. 21d to g).

NOTE: *thickness of blade; leather washer acts as a shock-absorber.*

Upper edges
ground away

(a)

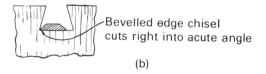

Bevelled edge chisel cuts right into acute angle

(b)

Fig. 283

## Firmer gouge (Figs. 285a and 188a)
(*outside* ground)
**Uses** Hollowing out (dishes, etc. – see Fig. 194).
Cutting accurate outside curves of small radius
(Fig. 285b).

## Scribing gouge (Figs. 286a and 188a)
(*inside* ground)
**Uses** Cutting accurate inside curves of small radius
(Figs. 106 and 107).
Scribing (cutting so as to fit together) mouldings
and moulded joints (Fig. 286b).

## Carving gouges (Fig. 188a to d)
Specially shaped gouges for wood removal in carving
– see Chapter 5.

## Turning gouges (Fig. 207a)
Very strongly made with long blade and handle.
Blades sharpened to a different end shape and angle
from standard gouges (see page 73).

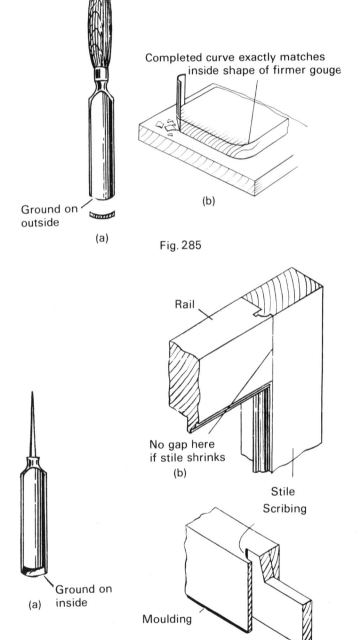

Completed curve exactly matches
inside shape of firmer gouge

Ground on
outside

(a)

(b)

Fig. 285

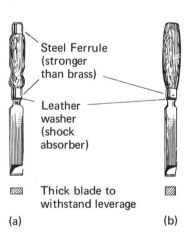

Steel Ferrule
(stronger
than brass)

Leather
washer
(shock
absorber)

 Thick blade to
withstand leverage

(a)

(b)

Fig. 284

Ground on
inside

(a)

Fig. 286

Rail

No gap here
if stile shrinks

(b)

Stile

Scribing

Moulding

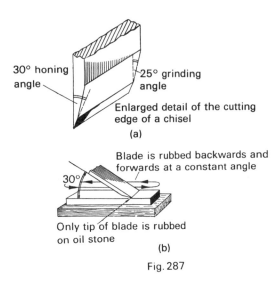

30° honing angle

25° grinding angle

Enlarged detail of the cutting edge of a chisel

(a)

Blade is rubbed backwards and forwards at a constant angle

30°

Only tip of blade is rubbed on oil stone

(b)

Fig. 287

## SHARPENING CHISEL AND PLANE BLADES

Chisel and plane blades are usually ground at 25° and honed (sharpened) at 30° (Fig. 287a). Having a second (honing) angle saves rubbing the whole of the ground surface of the blade on the oilstone when sharpening it (Fig. 287b).

**Grinding** is carried out either (a) on a sandstone (Fig. 288a), water being used to prevent the stone becoming clogged and to keep the blade cool, or (b) on a horizontally rotating artificial grinding stone, cooled with a special cutting oil (Fig. 288b).

Cool grinding is essential, for if the tool becomes overheated, it will lose its hardness. For this reason high speed dry grinding wheels are not normally used.

**Honing (sharpening on an oilstone),** to give the tool a fine edge, is carried out by rubbing it on an oilstone lubricated with thin machine or neatsfoot oil – *never* linseed oil. (This would clog the stone and prevent it from cutting.)

After rubbing the tool to and fro (at an angle of about 30°) as in Fig. 287b, a 'burr' will form at the tip of the blade (Fig. 289a). Remove this by rubbing the blade face down on the surface of the oilstone (Fig. 289b). If necessary, the blade should again be drawn backwards along the stone (Fig. 287b) to remove all traces of the burr and once more rubbed face down as in Fig. 289b.

NOTES:
(*a*) *always try to keep a constant honing angle and do not allow the tool to rock, for this will produce a rounded cutting edge.*
(*b*) *'ease' the sharp corners of plane blades as in Fig. 290a and b. The cutting edge of jack plane blades is slightly rounded as shown to make cutting easier when planing rough sawn timber to size.*

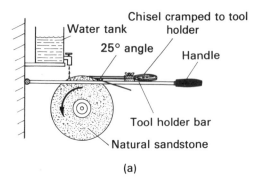

Water tank

Chisel cramped to tool holder

25° angle

Handle

Tool holder bar

Natural sandstone

(a)

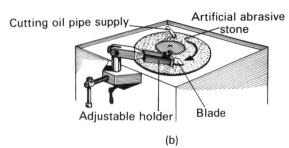

Cutting oil pipe supply

Artificial abrasive stone

Adjustable holder

Blade

(b)

Fig. 288

**Firmer gouges** are ground on an ordinary grindstone by rolling the blade from edge to edge so as to remove the metal evenly.

**Scribing gouges** are ground on specially shaped grinding wheels with rounded edges (Fig. 291). (In each case the grinding angle is 25°.)

**Turning gouges** are ground at an angle of about 40° and honed at the same angle. The corners of the tip of the blade are rounded off to prevent them from digging in while turning (Figs. 207a and 208).

NOTE: *the outer edge of gouge blades may be honed on an oilstone, but the inner curved face is honed by rubbing with a lubricated oilstone 'slip' of suitable shape (Fig. 292).*

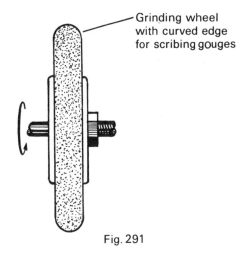

Grinding wheel with curved edge for scribing gouges

Fig. 291

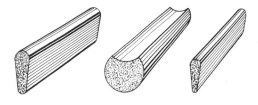

Fig. 292

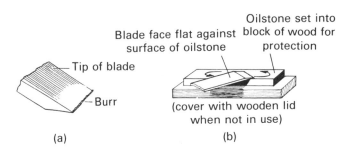

Tip of blade

Burr

Blade face flat against surface of oilstone

Oilstone set into block of wood for protection

(cover with wooden lid when not in use)

(a)                (b)

Fig. 289

(a)        (b)

Fig. 290

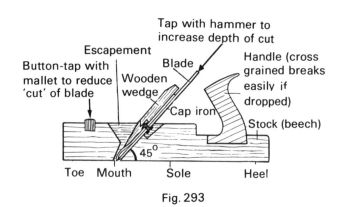

Fig. 293

## PLANES

The stock (body) of most types of plane may be either of wood (Fig. 293) or of metal (Fig. 294).

Metal planes are now widely used in school workshops (and elsewhere) because:

(a) they are easier to adjust than wooden planes;

(b) they are often easier to hold;

(c) they are less subject to wear on the 'sole' or 'mouth' than wooden planes;

(d) they are fitted with a tungsten steel type blade which gives a harder, longer lasting cutting edge than the cast steel blade fitted to wooden planes (Fig. 295).

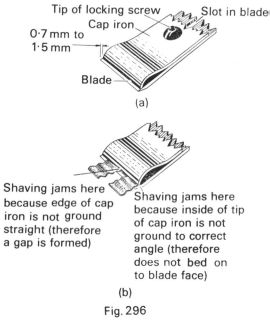

Fig. 296

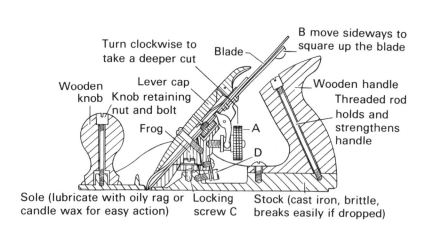

Fig. 294

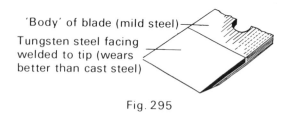

Fig. 295

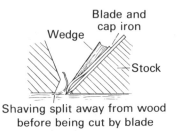

Fig. 297

## Cutting action and setting of bench planes (jack, trying and smoothing planes)

The thickness of the shavings and the smoothness of surface produced by a plane depends first upon the amount that the blade projects below the sole of the plane, and second on the distance the tip of the cap (back) iron is set behind the cutting edge of the blade (Fig. 296a). The closer it is set to the blade edge, the finer the shaving produced and the better the finish on the surface. A finely set blade (less than 1 mm) will be less likely to tear the grain than one which is coarsely set (2 mm). Fig. 296b shows two faults which may occur in this part of the plane.

Third, shavings and smoothness are also affected by the width of the plane mouth. Fig. 297 shows the effect of an over-wide mouth. Worn mouths on wooden planes have to be replaced (re-mouthed). On metal planes the width of the mouth can be adjusted by slackening the locking screws labelled C and screwing D (Fig. 294) in or out.

Fourth, the cutting edge of the blade must be parallel to the sole of the plane when viewed from the front (Fig. 298a and b). To correct the fault in Fig. 298b, for *wooden planes*, lightly tap the top corner of the blade sideways; and for *metal planes*, move lever B (Fig. 294) sideways. This will in each case pivot the blade sideways, thus squaring up the cutting edge of the blade.

**Jack plane** (300 mm to 400 mm long) (Fig. 293 shows a wooden jack)
**Use** Preparation of timber to size (see page 3) – a general purpose plane.

**Trying plane** (500 mm to 600 mm long)
**Use** Preparation of very accurate flat surfaces, e.g. rubbed butt joints (Fig. 37). The extra long sole cannot follow any unevenness or undulations in the surface of the wood (Fig. 299a and b). It touches only the points marked X, which are planed away until the whole surface becomes flat.

**Smoothing plane** (230 mm long) (Fig. 300 shows a wooden plane; Fig. 294 shows a metal plane)
**Uses** Cleaning up after gluing up.
    Trimming end grain, etc.

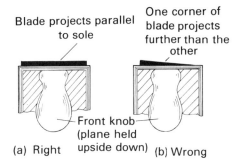

Blade projects parallel to sole

One corner of blade projects further than the other

Front knob (plane held upside down)

(a) Right    (b) Wrong

Fig. 298

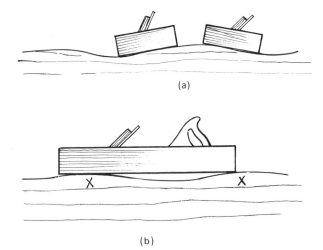

(a)

X          X

(b)

Fig. 299

Fig. 300

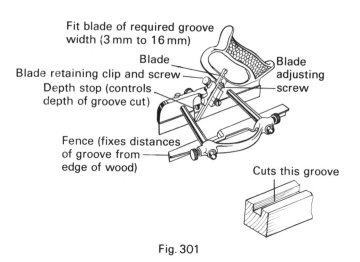

Fit blade of required groove
width (3 mm to 16 mm)

Blade

Blade retaining clip and screw

Depth stop (controls
depth of groove cut)

Blade
adjusting
screw

Fence (fixes distances
of groove from
edge of wood)

Cuts this groove

Fig. 301

## SPECIAL PURPOSE PLANES

### Plough plane (Fig. 301)

**Uses** Cutting grooves *along* the grain up to 16 mm
deep and 3 mm to 16 mm wide (Figs. 60b, 88, 132).
This plane will also cut rebates up to 16 mm wide.

### Rebate (rabbet) plane (Fig. 302).

**Uses** Cutting rebates (steps) along the grain (up to
32 mm wide) (Figs. 28, 82d, 124b). For rebating
across the grain it is advisable first to saw across the
grain (as in Fig. 19a) to prevent it from tearing.

### Shoulder plane (Fig. 303)

**Use** Accurately cutting or trueing rebates (will cut
across the grain or end grain) (Fig. 183b).

### Bull-nosed shoulder plane (Fig. 304)

**Use** 'One handed' cutting or trueing of rebates, etc.

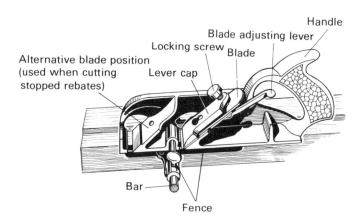

Handle

Blade adjusting lever

Locking screw   Blade

Alternative blade position
(used when cutting
stopped rebates)

Lever cap

Bar

Fence

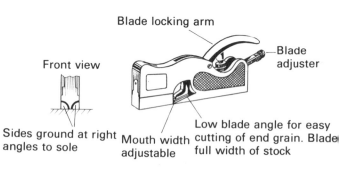

Blade locking arm

Front view

Blade
adjuster

Sides ground at right
angles to sole

Mouth width
adjustable

Low blade angle for easy
cutting of end grain. Blade
full width of stock

Fig. 303

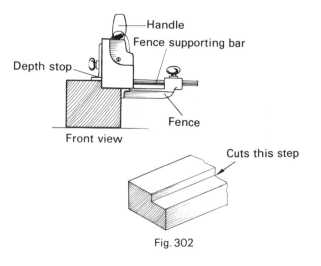

Handle

Fence supporting bar

Depth stop

Fence

Front view

Cuts this step

Fig. 302

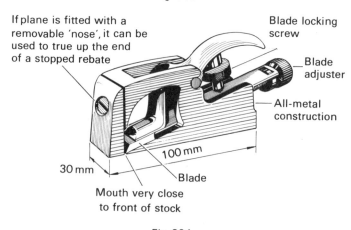

If plane is fitted with a
removable 'nose', it can be
used to true up the end
of a stopped rebate

Blade locking
screw

Blade
adjuster

All-metal
construction

100 mm

30 mm

Blade

Mouth very close
to front of stock

Fig. 304

**Moulding plane** (Figs. 305 and 182)
**Use** Cutting or trueing up mouldings. Each size and shape of moulding requires its own plane, as the shape of the sole and end of the blade is the exact reverse of the finished moulding shape (Fig. 175).

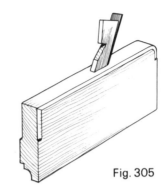

Fig. 305

**Router plane** (Fig. 306)
**Use** Cutting grooves or housings *across* the grain (Fig. 20a).

NOTE:
(*a*) *the sides of the housing must first be sawn (Fig. 19a and b);*
(*b*) *do not try to remove all waste wood from the housing with one cut. Set the blade to cut a shallow groove first, and then deepen it. (Lower the blade by turning the adjusting nut clockwise after slackening the thumb-screw. Retighten the thumb-screw before using.)*

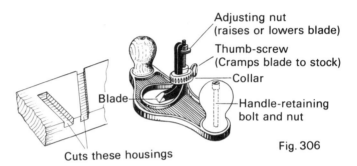

Fig. 306

**Spokeshave** (Fig. 307)
**Uses** Trueing curved work (page 40, and Figs. 108, 109, 110).
  Cutting chamfers (Fig. 174).
  Metal spokeshaves are easier to adjust than wooden ones and, as with planes, their soles and mouths do not wear so rapidly.

NOTE: *when using a spokeshave, do not have the blade too coarsely set; this will make the tool jump and give a very poor finish. Instead, use a fine blade-setting and work with a slow but firm sweeping action, trying always to keep the blade in contact with the work.*

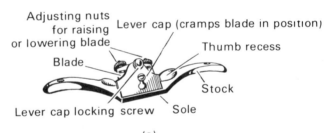

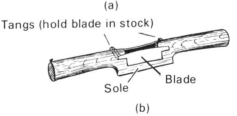

Fig. 307

**Toothing plane** (Fig. 308 – for the blade, see Fig. 156)
**Use** To roughen the surface of wood before veneering (Fig. 160). This helps the adhesive to 'key' the veneer firmly to the surface and so prevents its peeling off after drying out.

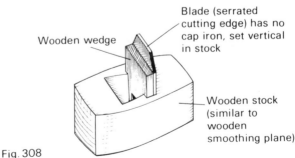

Fig. 308

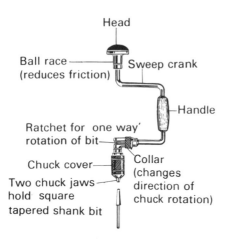

Head

Ball race (reduces friction)

Sweep crank

Handle

Ratchet for 'one way' rotation of bit

Chuck cover

Collar (changes direction of chuck rotation)

Two chuck jaws hold square tapered shank bit

Carpenter's ratchet brace

(a)

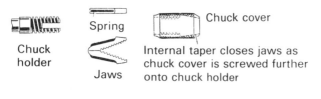

Chuck holder

Spring

Chuck cover

Jaws

Internal taper closes jaws as chuck cover is screwed further onto chuck holder

(b)

Fig. 309

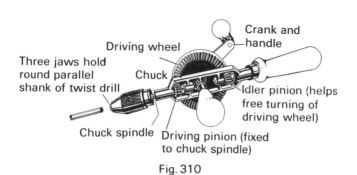

Crank and handle

Driving wheel

Three jaws hold round parallel shank of twist drill

Chuck

Idler pinion (helps free turning of driving wheel)

Chuck spindle

Driving pinion (fixed to chuck spindle)

Fig. 310

# BORING TOOLS

**Carpenter's ratchet brace** (Fig. 309)
**Use** Boring holes – with any square taper shank bit (Figs. 312 to 318).

NOTE: *where there is not enough space for a complete swing of the crank, the rachet is used. Twist the collar half a turn to left or right for clockwise or anticlockwise movement of the chuck. Fig. 309b shows how the chuck jaws are held and closed by the chuck cover.*

**Wheel brace** (Fig. 310)
**Uses** Boring holes of up to 8 mm in diameter with a round parallel shank twist drill (Fig. 311).

NOTE: *do not attempt to hold a square taper shank bit in a three-jaw chuck, or a round parallel shank drill in the chuck of a carpenter's brace.*

**Twist drill** (Fig. 311)
A metalworker's drill, useful for drilling screw-holes, etc., 1 mm to 8 mm in diameter. Cuts cleanly at any angle to the grain.

**Centre bit** (Fig. 312)
**Use** Boring holes in thin wood (not suitable for boring deep holes as it tends to 'wander' with the grain).

NOTES: *If boring right through work:*
*(a) work from one side until the bit centre just breaks through the back surface;*
*(b) turn the work over and complete the hole from the other side, otherwise the wood will be badly splintered as the bit breaks right through.*

**Improved (screw centre) bit** (Fig. 313)
**Use** As the centre bit (it requires less effort than the centre bit as the screw centre draws the bit into the work).

**Expanding bit** (Fig. 314)
**Use** As the centre bit. The expanding bit is a 'universal' bit which will cut 13 mm to 75 mm diameter holes. It has two interchangeable cutters to cover the range of diameters.

## TWIST BITS

**Irwin (solid centre) twist bit** (Fig. 315)
**Use** Boring deep holes along and across the grain.
The parallel sides prevent 'wandering' and the twin
spurs and cutters ensure a quick and easy boring
action.

**Jennings pattern twist bit** (Fig. 316)
**Use** As the solid centre bit, above.

**Forstner bit** (Fig. 317)
**Use** Boring flat bottomed blind (stopped) holes.

**Countersink (rose) bit** (Fig. 318)
**Use** To countersink holes to receive screw heads so
that they fit flush with the surface of the work
(Fig. 8b).

NOTE: *countersink bits are also available with round
shanks which fit into a wheel brace chuck.*

**Bradawl** (Fig. 319)
**Uses** Boring fine holes to take nails and making
pilot holes for screws in softwood (Fig. 9).

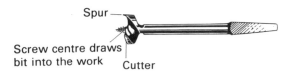

Spur
Screw centre draws
bit into the work
Cutter

Fig. 313

Fixed cutter
Adjustable cutter
and spur

Fig. 314

Two cutters
Parallel sides
Solid centre gives
extra strength

Fig. 315

Deeper flutes give good chip clearance

Fig. 316

Fig. 317

Fig. 318

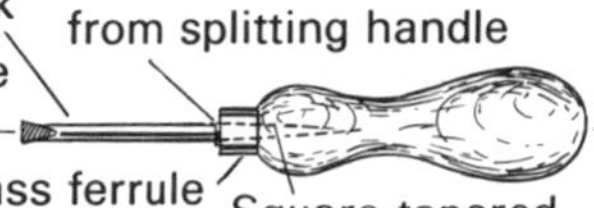

Flutes allow easy chip clearance
120°
Parallel sides
Round shank fits into
wheel-brace chuck

Fig. 311

Spur (nicker) first
cuts edge of hole
Pointed centre
Cutter (router) then
removes waste from hole
Tapered square
shank fits into
carpenter's brace chuck

Fig. 312

Shoulder prevents tang
from splitting handle
Shank
'Flared' cutting edge
gives clearance
for shank
Brass ferrule
Square tapered
tang
Handle
(ash or
beech)

Fig. 319

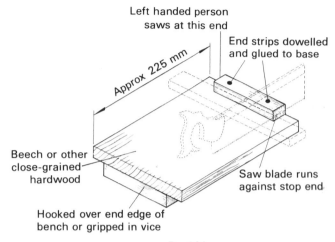

Left handed person
saws at this end

End strips dowelled
and glued to base

Approx 225 mm

Beech or other
close-grained
hardwood

Saw blade runs
against stop end

Hooked over end edge of
bench or gripped in vice

Fig. 320

## WORK-HOLDING EQUIPMENT

**Bench hook (sawing board)** (Fig. 320)
**Use** To steady strips of wood when cross cutting
with tenon saw (e.g. sawing to length, sawing tenon
shoulders).

**Mitre block and mitre box** (Fig. 321a and b)
**Use** Cutting accurate mitres (Fig. 321c) as used at
the corners of picture frames or boxes (Fig. 4a).
(The mitre box is an improved version of the mitre
block.)

**Shooting board** (Fig. 322)
**Use** To true end grain square to the face side and
edge of wood up to 100 mm wide. (For other
methods of planing end grain, see Fig. 3g, h and i.)

**Cradle** (Fig. 323)
**Uses** Supports strip or dowel while being planed or
chiselled.
    Enables square strip to be rounded.

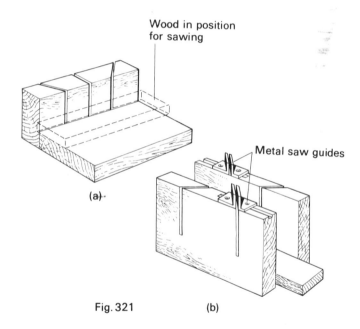

Wood in position
for sawing

Metal saw guides

(a)

(b)

Fig. 321

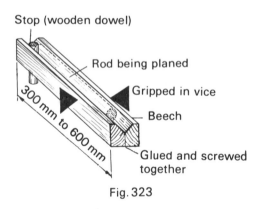

Stop (wooden dowel)

Rod being planed

Gripped in vice

300 mm to 600 mm

Beech

Glued and screwed
together

Fig. 323

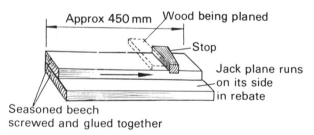

Approx 450 mm    Wood being planed

Stop

Jack plane runs
on its side
in rebate

Seasoned beech
screwed and glued together

Fig. 322

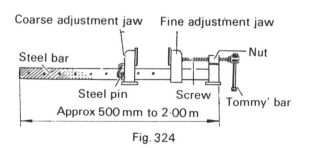

Coarse adjustment jaw    Fine adjustment jaw

Steel bar

Nut

Steel pin    Screw    Tommy' bar

Approx 500 mm to 2·00 m

Fig. 324

**Sash cramp** (Fig. 324)

**Use** Pulling joints tightly together when assembling work (Fig. 54a and b).

NOTE: *to prevent bruising the surface of the work, always put pads of scrap wood between it and the jaws, as in Fig. 54a.*

**G cramp** (Fig. 325)

**Uses** Holding work to bench top (Fig. 32h).

Cramping work together during or after assembly, or after gluing it (Fig. 58).

**Rack cramp** (Fig. 326)

**Uses** As the G cramp. (The rack cramp adjusts quickly over a large range of jaw openings.)

**F cramp** (Fig. 327)

**Uses** As the G cramp. (It has quick-action coarse adjustment of moving jaw.)

NOTE: *the deep 'throat'.*

**Handscrew** (Fig. 328)

**Uses** As the G cramp. This is the traditional woodworking cramp. As all parts are made of wood, the threads of the screws and nuts tend to wear badly. It has now been largely replaced by the metal cramps described above.

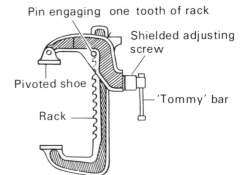

Fig. 326

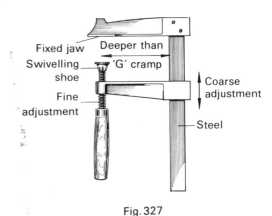

Fig. 327

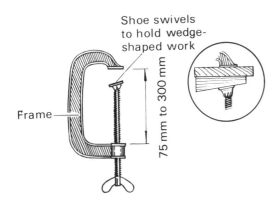

Fig. 325

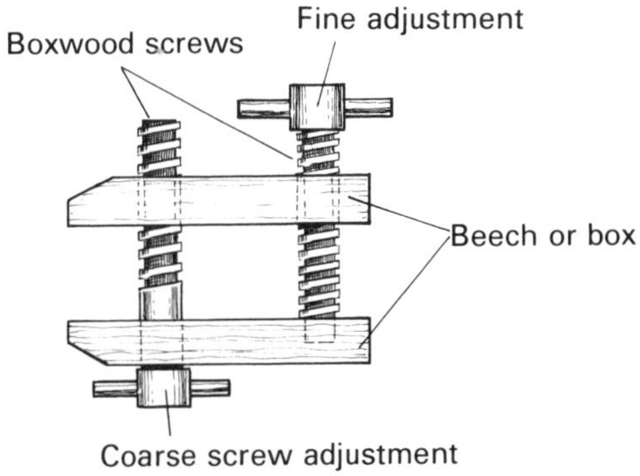

Fig. 328

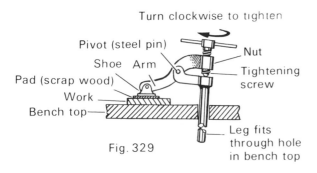

Turn clockwise to tighten

Pivot (steel pin)

Nut

Shoe   Arm

Tightening screw

Pad (scrap wood)

Work

Bench top

Leg fits through hole in bench top

Fig. 329

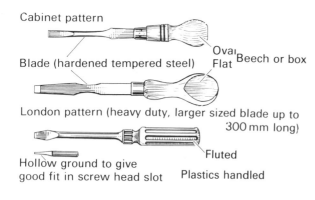

Cabinet pattern

Blade (hardened tempered steel)

Oval   Beech or box
Flat

London pattern (heavy duty, larger sized blade up to 300 mm long)

Hollow ground to give good fit in screw head slot

Fluted

Plastics handled

(a)

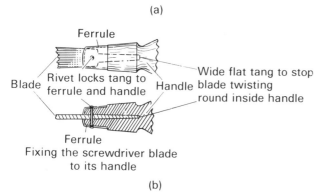

Ferrule

Rivet locks tang to ferrule and handle

Blade

Handle

Wide flat tang to stop blade twisting round inside handle

Ferrule

Fixing the screwdriver blade to its handle

(b)

Fig. 330

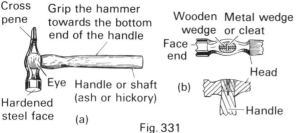

Cross pene

Grip the hammer towards the bottom end of the handle

Wooden wedge

Metal wedge or cleat

Face end

Head

Eye   Handle or shaft (ash or hickory)

(b)

Hardened steel face

(a)

Handle

Fig. 331

**Bench holdfast** (Fig. 329)

**Uses** Cramping wood to the bench top while sawing or chiselling it. The nut is raised when the tightening screw is turned clockwise (screwed further through it). This forces the shoe down on to the work (the leg behaves rather like a see-saw).

## MISCELLANEOUS TOOLS

**Screwdrivers** (Fig. 330a)

**Use** Inserting and removing screws (Fig. 10a and b).

NOTE: *method of fixing blade to handle (Fig. 330b).*

**Hammers**

**Warrington hammer** (Fig. 331a)

**Uses** Knocking in nails (Figs. 4, 5 and 6).
   Assembling joints (Fig. 53b).
   Setting the blades of wooden planes (Fig. 293).
The cross pene is used for:
   Laying cross-banding and inlaid lines (Figs. 164b and 170b).
   'Starting' small nails.

NOTE: *how the head is fixed to the handle (Fig. 331b):*
*(a) the end of the handle is narrowed down to pass through the hole in the head (which has a double taper);*
*(b) a wooden wedge is driven in lengthways to spread the end of the handle sideways;*
*(c) a metal wedge (cleat) is driven in crossways. This spreads the handle lengthways and locks the wooden wedge in position.*

SAFETY NOTE: *loose hammer heads are dangerous. Always be sure that they are wedged tightly to their handles.*

**Pin hammer** (Fig. 332)

**Uses** Driving in panel pins and fine nails (Fig. 4).

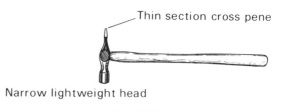

Thin section cross pene

Narrow lightweight head

Fig. 332

**Claw hammer** (Fig. 333a)
**Uses** Knocking in and removing nails (with the claw) as in Fig. 333b.

NOTE: *fitted with a thicker, stronger handle than the Warrington pattern hammer, to withstand leverage when removing nails.*

**Mallets**
**Woodworker's mallet** (Fig. 334a)
**Use** Driving chisels when cutting joints, etc.

NOTE: *the method of fitting the head. It cannot be wedged on like a hammer head as it would split. When the mallet is swung (Fig. 334b), the head tends to fly off the handle. By tapering the handle and the hole through the head (Fig. 334c), the head grips the handle more firmly each time the mallet is used. To remove the head, tap the bottom end of the mallet handle sharply on the bench top or floor. The head will be jerked loose and can be slid down the handle (Fig. 334c).*

**Carver's mallet** (Fig. 190)
**Use** Rounded head specially designed for use in wood carving (see Chapter 5).

**Pincers** (Fig. 335)
**Use** Withdrawing nails (Fig. 335b).

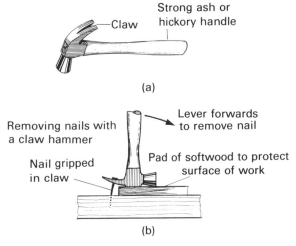

Fig. 333

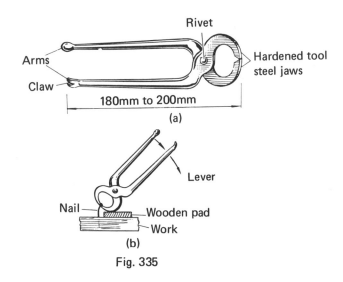

Fig. 335

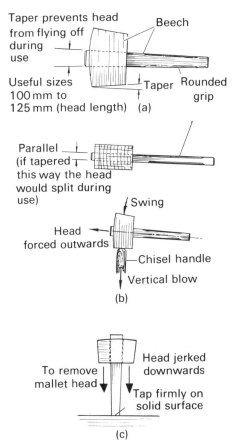

Fig. 334

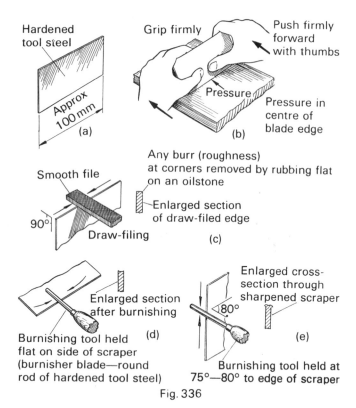

Fig. 336

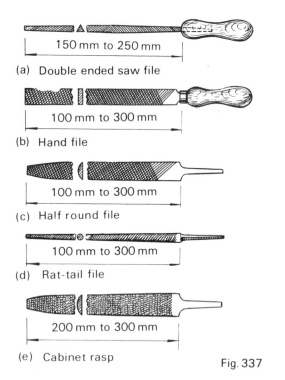

(a) Double ended saw file
150 mm to 250 mm

(b) Hand file
100 mm to 300 mm

(c) Half round file
100 mm to 300 mm

(d) Rat-tail file
100 mm to 300 mm

(e) Cabinet rasp
200 mm to 300 mm

Fig. 337

## Scratch stock (Figs. 170a and 184)
**Uses** Making narrow grooves for inlay lines.
Forming mouldings on edges of work.

## Scraper (Figs. 336 and 193)
**Uses** Smoothing difficult surface grain before final glasspapering (Fig. 336b).
Cleaning up veneered work.
Cleaning up hollows in carved work (Fig. 195e).

NOTE: *a blunt scraper is almost useless. Sharpened, as in Fig. 336c, d and e, it will cut fine shavings without tearing the grain.*

## Files (Fig. 337 a to d)
## Saw file
**Use** Filing the teeth of saws to the correct shape (Figs. 274c and 275b).

## Hand, half round and rat tail files
These are examples of metalworkers' files which are useful for maintenance of tools, adjusting metal fittings, etc.

## Cabinet rasp (Fig. 337e)
**Use** Roughing down shaped work (often used in carving).

SAFETY NOTE: *always fit a handle to a file before using it. A sharp tang can easily pierce the palm of the hand – apart from being uncomfortable to hold.*

## Surform rasp (Fig. 338)
**Use** Rough shaping work. As the teeth are cut right through the specially hardened blade, they do not clog easily like those of an ordinary rasp. Worn blades are replaceable.

Fig. 338

# 10 Powered Tools

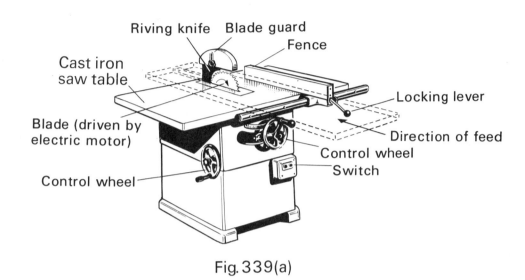

Riving knife · Blade guard
Fence
Cast iron
saw table
Blade (driven by
electric motor)
Locking lever
Direction of feed
Control wheel
Switch
Control wheel

Fig. 339(a)

On the manufacturing side of the woodworking industry, nearly all aspects of practical work have been mechanised. Thus the mass-production methods employed in the making of items of woodwork (ranging from greenhouses to furniture) rarely call for timber preparation, jointing, or assembling to be carried out using traditional hand methods. Instead, a wide range of electrically-powered machine tools carry out the work more quickly, more cheaply and, sometimes, more accurately.

This chapter deals with three types of powered equipment:
    basic fixed machines;
    portable tools;
  'do it yourself' attachments for portable electric
    drills.

NOTE: *before using powered tools, ALWAYS obtain practical instruction on their use.*

## FIXED MACHINERY

The following machines are often employed in school and small industrial workshops.

**Circular saw** (Fig. 339)
This is used for ripping and cross-cutting timber accurately to size. The blade, whose diameter ranges from 200 mm to 600 mm or more, revolves at speeds of up to 3000 revolutions per minute (rev/min). The important factor here is the peripheral speed (the speed at the cutting edge), which is generally about 2500 metres per minute.

Because of this very high cutting speed, and the fact that wood may be 'snatched' by the saw blade teeth during the cutting operation, circular saws are potentially most dangerous unless used with extreme caution. For this reason, pupils are not normally permitted to use them in school workshops.

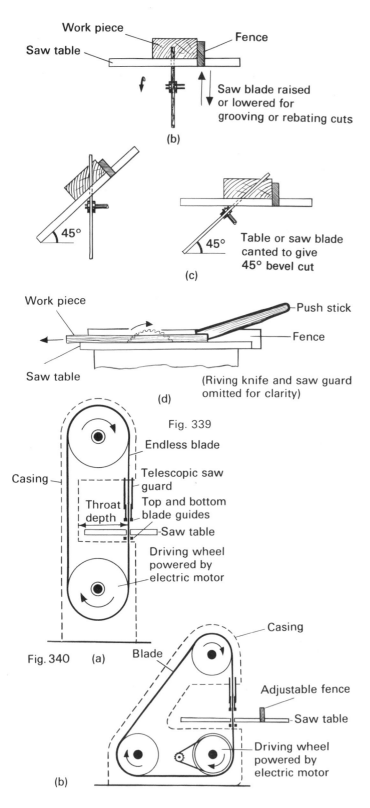

**Work piece**
**Saw table**
**Fence**
Saw blade raised or lowered for grooving or rebating cuts

(b)

45°

45°   Table or saw blade canted to give 45° bevel cut

(c)

**Work piece**
Push stick
Fence
**Saw table**
(Riving knife and saw guard omitted for clarity)

(d)

Fig. 339

Endless blade
Telescopic saw guard
Top and bottom blade guides
Casing
Throat depth
Saw table
Driving wheel powered by electric motor

Fig. 340   (a)   Blade

Casing
Adjustable fence
Saw table
Driving wheel powered by electric motor

(b)

Fig. 339a shows the main features of a circular saw. On most circular saws the blade can be raised or lowered to adjust the depth of cut when making a rebate or groove (Fig. 339b). Often it can also be tilted at an angle of up to 45° to enable bevel cuts to be made (Fig. 339c). Rip, cross-cut, or combination (general purpose) blades are available.

## Basic rules for use

(a) Wood should never be cut until the blade is revolving at full speed.
(b) Do not apply too much pressure to force the wood past the blade – allow the saw to cut at its own rate.
(c) A push stick should ALWAYS be used for moving the wood past or near the blade, NEVER the hand (Fig. 339d).
(d) A blunt blade is inefficient and likely to prove dangerous – see (b) above.

## Band saw (Fig. 340a, b and c)

The band saw, as its name suggests, has a long, narrow, endless blade which passes round two, or sometimes three, wheels (Fig. 340a and b). Because the blade is narrow (6 mm to 18 mm wide), this saw is used for cutting curves and for shaping generally.

Blades of differing tooth pitch are available for cutting wood, metal and plastics. If a fence is cramped to the work table, wood may be ripped to width, although not so accurately as with a circular saw.

The throat depth (Fig. 340a) determines the width of work which can be sawn, and, as on most circular saws, the table can be tilted for bevel cutting, as in Fig. 340c, which shows a bench-mounted band saw.

## Basic rules for use

Before using:

(a) Ensure that the blade is correctly tensioned and lined up on its wheels.

(b) Check that the top and bottom blade guides are correctly positioned, with the top guides set as low as is convenient for cutting.

Cutting:

(c) Allow the blade to reach full speed before feeding in the work, and do not try to make it cut too quickly.

(d) When cutting 'sharp' curves, do not twist the wood round too rapidly or the blade will be strained and will probably break.

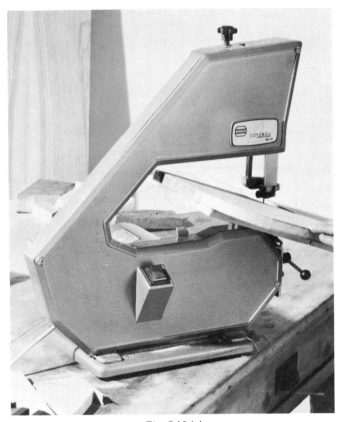

Fig. 340 (c)

## Jig saw (Fig. 341)

The jig or scroll saw is the mechanised 'big brother' of the fret saw. The blade cuts on the 'down' stroke only and therefore the work piece has to be held down to the table by an adjustable spring 'hold-down' fork. This is carefully set so that it allows the work to slide underneath it, but prevents it from being lifted off the table on the 'up' or return stroke.

The blades, which are about the size of coping saw blades, are fairly brittle, so care must be taken not to force the work when cutting sharp curves.

As with the bandsaw, blades of different width and tooth pitch are available. Thus, when fitted with the appropriate blade, either of these saws can cut hardwoods and softwoods, plastics, and even thin sheet metal. 'Sabre' blades, which are gripped only at their lower end, may be used when cutting holes and enclosed shapes.

## Basic rules for use

(a) Ensure that the correct blade is fitted and properly tensioned.

(b) Adjust the hold-down fork to suit the thickness of the material to be sawn.

(c) Do not force the work into the saw blade, especially when changing the direction of cut – for example, at a corner, or when sawing a curve of small radius.

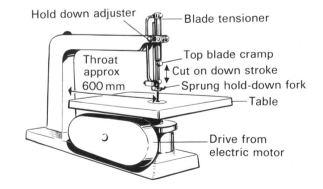

Fig. 341

**Planer** (Fig. 342)

The planer and planer thicknesser (which also prepares timber to thickness) does not work like a hand plane. The wood is fed against a very fast rotating cutter block into which are locked two, three, or four cutting blades (Fig. 342a). The cutter block and blades are from 100 mm to 500 mm long, and this length determines the maximum width of wood which can be planed on the machine.

With the cutter block rotating at between 4000 and 6000 rev/min a series of shallow cuts is taken (Fig. 342b) as the wood is fed over it. Thus, the slower the feed rate (of wood over cutter block), the greater the number of cuts per metre, and therefore the smoother the finish obtained.

The depth of cut is regulated by adjustment of the height of the front and back tables.

**Basic rules for use**

(a) Check the depth of cut before switching on.
(b) Allow the cutter block to attain full speed before feeding the wood slowly but firmly over it.
(c) NEVER pass the hands over the exposed cutter block. Many planer operators have lost fingers and even hands when these have slipped into the revolving blades.

Instead, cover the exposed cutter block with the safety guard, and change the position of the hands so that they *never* pass over the cutter block, even on top of the wood being planed.
(d) Wood should be cut *with* the grain (Fig. 342c). Cutting into or against the grain (Fig. 342d) will cause it to tear badly.

Pupils are not allowed to use planer machines in school workshops because of their potential danger.

**Vertical drill** (Fig. 343)

The pillar (floor-standing) or bench drill, or drill press as it is sometimes called, was originally designed for metalworking, but has useful applications in the woodwork shop. Fig. 343a shows its main features. The multi-step pulley blocks provide a range of speeds to suit different drilling conditions. The table is adjustable for height, and by means of a rack and pinion mechanism, anticlockwise rotation of the feed arms lowers the drill chuck, thus feeding the drill into the work.

Machine planed surface (rippled effect exaggerated for clarity)

(b)

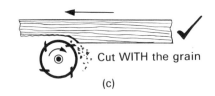

Cut WITH the grain

(c)

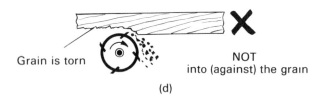

Grain is torn

NOT into (against) the grain

(d)

Fig 342

Small diameter holes may be bored into wood using standard metal twist drills (Fig. 311). For holes over 6 mm diameter, special high-speed wood bits are available, with parallel shanks which may be securely gripped in the Jacobs pattern drill chuck with which these drilling machines are usually fitted. NOTE: *a chuck guard, usually made of a clear plastics, should always be fitted, as metal slivers sometimes run up the twist drill flutes and may be thrown outwards. These could cause very serious eye injury. The guard also prevents long hair, loose shirt cuffs, and any other dangling items of clothing, from being caught up by the drill chuck.*

Attachments are available for converting the vertical drill into a morticing machine. Essentially this attachment consists of a strong twist bit which rotates inside a closely-fitting square section tube. The lower end of this tube is ground on its inside faces like a set of four chisel blades (Fig. 343b) which 'square off' the round hole bored out by the rotating solid centre twist bit. The work is solidly cramped against a fence which fits on to the drill table.

## Basic rules for use

Before switching on:

(a) Always ensure that the drill bit is tightly gripped in the chuck, and remove the chuck tightening key before use.

(b) Rotate the chuck and drill bit by hand to make sure that the drill bit has been correctly centred and rotates freely.

(c) Cramp the workpiece to the drill table. If small pieces of metal or wood are to be drilled, use a machine vice.

NOTE: *failure to secure the work may lead to serious accident. The work, if held only by the hand, may be ripped from the grasp and the fingers injured. It may also be thrown from the machine with considerable force and possibly cause further damage, or injury to others. Additionally, the drill bit will almost certainly be damaged or broken.*

(d) Always have the chuck guard in position.

(e) Check that the drill speed is suitable for (i) the material being cut; (ii) the type of drill bit being used; (iii) the diameter of the hole being cut. Remember – the larger the drill bit diameter, the slower should be the rev/min.

Multi-step pulley system inside head casing

Motor

Feed handle

Jacobs pattern chuck

Column

Chuck guard

Table

Base

(a)

Non-rotating square tube

Chisel edges cut the mortice sides

Rotating twist bit cuts centre of square mortice and removes chips

Bored out by twist bit

Trimmed out by chisel edges

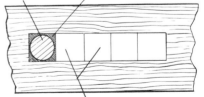

Attachment cuts a series of square holes, thus, to cut a mortice

(b)

Fig. 343

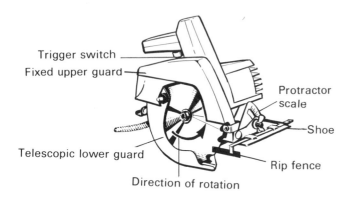

Trigger switch
Fixed upper guard
Telescopic lower guard
Direction of rotation
Protractor scale
Shoe
Rip fence

Fig. 344(a)

## PORTABLE POWERED TOOLS

Portable powered tools, while smaller and often less powerful than fixed woodworking machines, have an important part to play in many woodworking activities, some being of particular value in 'on site' building work as well as in the workshop.

**Circular saw** (Fig. 344a)

Portable circular saws are fitted with blades of 150 mm to 215 mm diameter, usually of the combination type which can be used both to rip and cross cut timber. A telescopic lower blade guard covers the saw teeth (except those actually in contact with the timber). Note that the saw teeth cut upwards through the board. This helps to hold the body of the saw tightly on to the top of the workpiece.

The rip fence enables strips to be cut parallel to the edge of a board, and depth adjustment ensures that the saw teeth just break through the underside of the work. Bevel cuts can be made by locking on the appropriate part of the protractor scale, thus tilting the saw shoe.

**Basic rules for use**

(a) Ensure that the work is securely fixed to a trestle or bench, with a clear space in which to operate the saw for the full length of the cut.

(b) Check that the lower guard is operating freely, and that the rip fence and depth of cut are correctly adjusted. See, too, that the cable is kept well away from the saw blade.

(c) Rest the front of the saw shoe on the end of the board where it is to cut, and switch on by squeezing the trigger. Allow the saw blade to reach full rev/min before advancing the saw firmly but steadily into the work.

(d) Keep the saw cut quite straight or the blade will tend to bind in the work.

(e) Do not switch off while the saw blade is still cutting. First remove the saw from the wood. Then switch off and wait for the blade to stop rotating before putting the saw down.

(f) Disconnect the saw cable from the electricity supply as soon as you have finished sawing. This applies to all portable powered tools.

## Jig saw (Fig. 344b)

Portable jig saws are invaluable for quick cutting of curved shapes in large sheets of plywood, chipboard, and so on, when the size of the work is too large for it to be cut on a fixed jig saw machine.

The short blade cuts on the 'up' stroke, thus helping to keep the saw body pulled down firmly on to the work. A built-in 'puffer' blows the sawdust away from the cutting area.

### Basic rules for use

(a) Ensure that the blade fitted is suitable for the material being cut and that it is securely locked to its holder.
(b) Provide adequate support – over the end of a bench – for the work, and, if possible, cramp it to the bench top.
(c) Switch on and guide the saw along previously pencilled guide lines (Fig. 344b).
(d) Remove the saw from the work before switching off.
(e) If holes or internal shapes are to be produced, pre-bore the work so that the saw blade can be inserted before starting the cut.

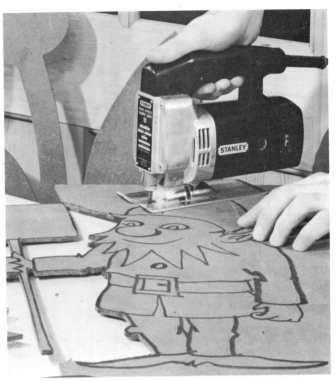

Fig. 344 (b)

## Plane (Fig. 345)

Working on the same principle as the fixed planing machine (Fig. 342), portable power planes are widely used for 'on site' work.

Their length, 375 mm to 450 mm, is comparable to that of a jack or short trying plane. The two-bladed cutter block, 80 mm to 130 mm wide, has a depth of cut of up to 3 mm, and revolves at speeds in the region of 15 000 rev/min.

### Basic rules for use

(a) Before switching on, after adjusting the depth of cut, rest the front half of the sole on the wood to be planed, so that the cutter block is just clear of the end of the board. The board must, of course, be adequately supported.
(b) Switch on, using the trigger switch mounted on the handle, and allow cutter speed to build up before pushing the plane smoothly forward.
(c) Plane with the grain as with a hand plane. Very little pressure is required to push the plane forward.

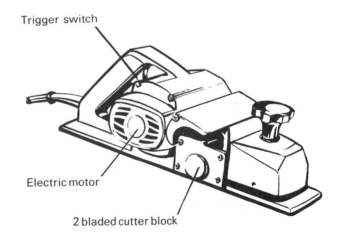

Trigger switch

Electric motor

2 bladed cutter block

Fig. 345

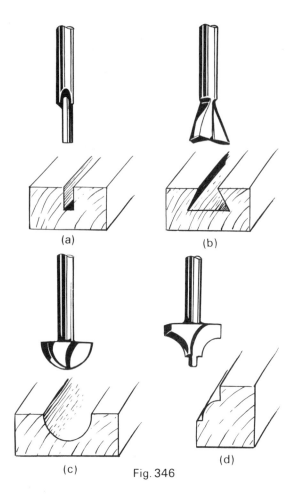

(a)          (b)

(c)        Fig. 346        (d)

(d) Do not switch off until the plane is clear of the work.
(e) Allow time for the cutter to stop rotating before putting the plane down. Remember that cutter blades are easily damaged by misuse and careless storage.

**Router** (Fig. 346)

The router is a high-speed shaping tool used for grooving, slot morticing, rebating, and housing. When fitted with appropriately-shaped cutters it can also be used to 'carve' or work mouldings.

Essentially it consists of an electric motor-driven chuck rotating at about 20 000 rev/min, and a base, fitted with two handles, which is cramped to the motor casing. A range of cutters, examples of which are shown in Fig. 346, can be fitted into the chuck.

A guide fence, shown in Fig. 346e, is used when cutting parallel to an edge (as in grooving or slot morticing), or for circular work. Templates are used to guide the router cutter when shaped work is required.

**Basic rules for use**

(a) Do not attempt to adjust the machine or change the cutter without first disconnecting the router from the electricity supply.
(b) Carefully follow the manufacturer's instructions when changing the cutter or adjusting the depth of cut.
(c) Whenever possible, rest the router sole flat on the work with the cutter just clear of the wood before switching on, and allow the cutter to reach full speed before feeding it steadily into the work.'
(d) When routing hardwoods, it may be necessary to make several cuts at increasing depths before the final cut is made.
(e) As with any woodworking tool, cutters must be kept razor-sharp. Blunt cutters will leave a poor finish on the work and may overload and damage the motor.

Fig. 346 (e)

## Sanders

Three basic types of sanders are made.

(a) **Belt sander** (Fig. 347)

The belt sander is particularly useful when a good deal of wood is to be removed from the surface, or large surfaces are to be sanded. It works rather like a high speed continuously cutting file. The sanding belt, coated with aluminium oxide (see also Chapter 7, page 78), passes round the two rollers at very high speed, even pressure being applied to the work by the plate P. Waste dust is collected in the bag as in a vacuum cleaner. This type of sander is much more expensive than types (b) and (c), and its use is usually limited to production workshops.

(b) **Disc sander** (Fig. 348)

The disc sander may be used for sanding and shaping wood, or removing rust, etc., from metal. It is best employed for coarse work or where localised areas require a good deal of attention.

The abrasive disc, 125 mm to 175 mm diameter, usually of the aluminium oxide coated variety, is fixed to a flexible rubber backing pad by means of a large dished washer and screw.

If required, portable disc sanders can be converted to fixed sanders by (i) attaching a suitable stand and sanding table; and (ii) changing the rubber backing pad for a flat metal pad to which the abrasive disc is glued (Fig. 351b).

## Basic rules for use

(a) Wear a face shield or visor to protect the eyes from dust. If working indoors, or removing old paint or varnish, a simple dust mask should also be worn.
(b) Ensure that the abrasive (sanding) disc is securely fixed to the backing pad.
(c) Hold the tool clear of the work and switch on.
(d) Move the sander across the work with steady sweeping strokes, holding it at a slight angle to the work so that only one side of the abrasive disc touches the surface. If the whole face of the abrasive disc touches the work it will be difficult to control.
(e) Use only light pressure.

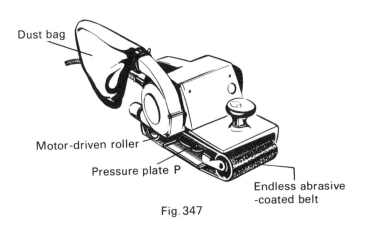

Dust bag

Motor-driven roller

Pressure plate P

Endless abrasive -coated belt

Fig. 347

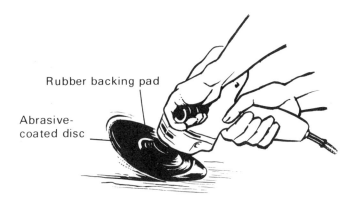

Rubber backing pad

Abrasive- coated disc

Fig. 348

(f) The sander should be moved continuously along or across the face of the work to avoid oversanding or scoring in any one spot.

(g) When using the fixed sander attachment (Fig. 351b), sand and shape only on the downward cutting side of the disc face.

NOTE: *because the sanding action is in a circular direction this type of sander is not really suitable for preparing surfaces which are to be polished, clear lacquered, or varnished as the sanding marks will show through.*

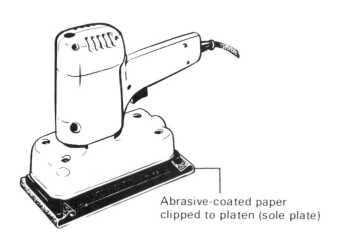

Abrasive-coated paper clipped to platen (sole plate)

Fig. 349

### (c) Orbital sander (Fig. 349)

This type of sander is designed to give a fine satin-smooth surface suitable for polishing. It is generally unsuitable for coarse sanding except on softwoods. The platen (sole plate to which the abrasive sheet is clipped) moves at high speed in very small circles. These circles are so small (3 mm to 4 mm diameter) that the cross grain scratches imparted to the work are too fine to be noticed.

### Basic rules for use

(a) Check that the abrasive paper is securely clipped to the platen.

(b) Hold the sander clear of the work and switch on.

(c) Sand in any direction but do not press – the sander's own weight is enough.

(d) Do not over-sand edges which have been veneered or lipped. Veneers are so thin that it is easy to sand right through them.

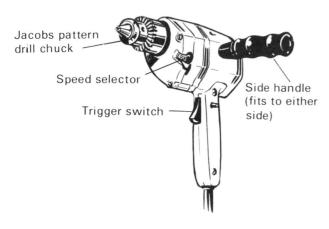

Jacobs pattern drill chuck

Speed selector

Trigger switch

Side handle (fits to either side)

Fig. 350 (a)

### Portable drill (Fig. 350a)

A large range of portable electric drills is produced which, depending upon the power of the motor and the capacity of the chuck, will take metal twist drills of up to 12 mm diameter.

Most small drills of 6 mm to 8 mm capacity have speeds of between 800 and 2750 rev/min. Many are two-speed drills, the lower speed being generally used when drilling metal and brick, etc., and the higher one for drilling small holes in wood.

## Basic rules for use

(a) Disconnect the drill from the power supply when changing drill bits.

(b) Ensure that the drill bit shank is gripped centrally by all three chuck jaws and lock the chuck tightly with the chuck key. As with the vertical drilling machine, remember to remove the chuck key before switching on!

(c) Always support the work. Small work should be held in a vice or G cramped to the bench.

(d) Use a centre punch mark to fix the centre of holes when drilling metals, and a nail hole to start a drill hole in wood accurately (Fig. 350b). This will prevent the drill point from wandering as it starts to cut.

(e) When boring a hole, apply just sufficient pressure to keep the tool cutting. Too much force may overload the motor, causing it to slow down considerably and overheat.

If difficulty is encountered (i) check that the drill bit is sharp – if not, regrind it before using it again; (ii) ensure, particularly when boring wood, that the flutes have not become choked with waste material.

(f) When drilling metals (except brass and cast iron), lubricate the drill point with a little light machine oil.

(g) If using a two-speed drill, do not change from one speed to another until the drill has stopped.

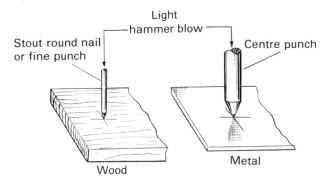

Fig. 350 (b)

## 'DO IT YOURSELF' ATTACHMENTS FOR PORTABLE POWERED DRILLS

In school workshops individual portable powered tools, saws, drills, sanders, etc., are preferred, but at home one source of power – the electric drill – is often used to drive a number of purpose-made attachments. Most portable drill manufacturers make a range of attachments to suit their own drills, and generally speaking it is best to purchase the attachments made specifically for that particular make of drill.

Bear in mind that smaller capacity drills (6 mm to 8 mm) do not have the power of, say, a standard portable saw, and therefore cannot be used for very heavy cutting. Within these limitations 'do it yourself' portable drill attachments can be very

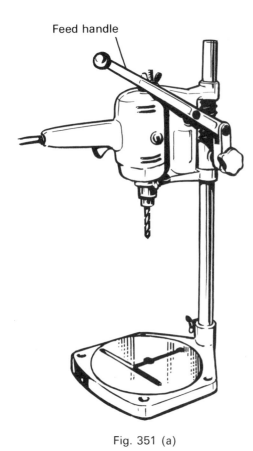

Feed handle

Fig. 351 (a)

useful and time saving. If you anticipate using these attachments with a portable drill, buy the most powerful model you can afford.

### Circular saw attachment

Apart from the lower power and smaller diameter saw blade (usually 125 mm diameter), the drill with saw attachment is used in the same way as the standard portable power saw (Fig. 344).

### Additional points to note

(a) Be sure that the attachment is firmly secured to the drill body before plugging in to the power point and switching on.

(b) Do not try to cut wood which is too thick, nor overload the motor by forcing the blade in an attempt to cut too quickly.

(c) Small saw tables are available to which portable drills with sawing attachments can be fitted. Some of these tables are not supplied with a saw blade guard, and the top of the saw blade is partly exposed. This is potentially very dangerous, and a saw table of this type should be used with the greatest care!

### Jig saw attachment

This, once fitted to the drill, is used in exactly the same way as the standard model (Fig. 344b). Points (a) and (b) above, concerning circular saw attachments also apply here.

### Vertical drill stand (Fig. 351a)

When working at home, where a vertical drill (Fig. 343a) is not usually available, a vertical drill stand has much to commend it. It gives better control over direction and general accuracy in drilling where the work is narrow enough to fit on to the table.

### Sanding attachments

Both circular and orbital sanding attachments are available. A horizontal drill stand and disc sanding table attachment (Fig. 351b) will convert the drill into an efficient disc sander. Note the adjustable fence for accurately sanding mitres.

Fig. 351 (b)

## SAFETY PRECAUTIONS

### Conduct in the workshop

It cannot be over-emphasised that any powered woodworking tool, simply because it is powered, is potentially much more dangerous than its hand-powered counterpart.

The remarks made in Chapter 1 (page 1) about dress and workshop conduct generally are of even greater importance when powered equipment is being used.

As when a lathe is in use (Chapter 6), never chat to anyone using powered machinery: you may distract his attention and cause an accident. If working with powered tools at home, always be sure someone else is on hand – just in case!

### Electrical safety

In school workshops, safety switches of the push off variety are provided for all machines. Additionally, emergency circuit switches are situated in various parts of the workshop which, when pressed, will cut off the electrical power supply to all fixed machinery.

If you see someone in trouble with a machine, do not wait for your teacher to do something about it. AT ONCE – CUT OFF THE POWER SUPPLY at the nearest emergency switch (always painted red).

Portable powered equipment uses either the standard 230 volts mains supply, or, in some school workshops, a stepped-down supply at 110 volts. This lower voltage considerably reduces the chance of severe electrical shock should the operator touch a 'live' wire or tool.

Before plugging in portable tools, check that the tool and supply voltage are both the same.

Fixed power tools are permanently wired into the mains electricity supply, but portable tools are usually plugged into 13 amp socket outlets.

As metals are good conductors of electricity, in case of a breakdown in the electrical insulation of the tool, 3 pin fused plugs (live, neutral and earth) are used and are wired up to the tool cable (see Fig. 352a and b). Hard rubber plugs are best, for they do not break if dropped.

Ten amp fuses are required for most portable power tools, but the manufacturer's detailed instructions should always be followed.

'Old' colour code

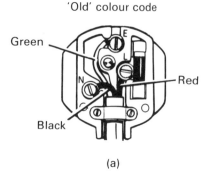

Green

Red

Black

(a)

'New' colour code (introduced in 1970)

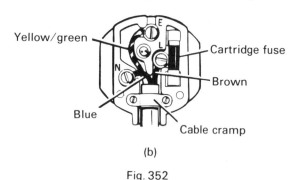

Yellow/green

Cartridge fuse

Brown

Blue

Cable cramp

(b)

Fig. 352

Some modern drills and other tools are encased entirely in tough plastics materials so that it is impossible to get a shock from them. In these cases only two core cable (live and neutral) is provided, and the earth pin connection on the plug is not used.

Always remove the plug from the supply socket before making any adjustment to the tool. While it is obvious commonsense not to use electrical equipment in wet or damp conditions, it is not from the tool itself that the operator is likely to receive an electric shock, but from a faulty cable.

Frayed insulation or loosened plug connections are the usual cause of such accidents. For this reason check regularly that (a) power leads (cables) are in good condition with no cuts or fraying of the insulation, and (b) the plug connections and cable cramps are tight (see Fig. 352).

Avoid damage by:

(a) not dragging or scuffing cables;

(b) not removing plugs from their socket outlets by pulling on the cable;

(c) coiling cables to avoid damage when the tool is not in use; and

(d) whenever possible, working with the cable behind you rather than in front, to avoid accidentally damaging it with the tool.

If extension cables are used, joints should NOT be made by twisting the wires together and binding them with adhesive tape. Cable connectors of the correct type should ALWAYS be used. Fig. 353 shows the right way to extend a power cable. Be careful to use the correct grade of cable when making up such an extension. If in doubt, consult your teacher, or a qualified electrician.

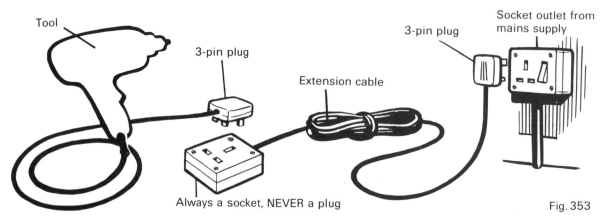

Tool

3-pin plug

Extension cable

3-pin plug

Socket outlet from mains supply

Always a socket, NEVER a plug

Fig. 353

# 11 Design and Planning

Designing or planning consists of thinking about and solving *all* the problems connected with the making and future use of the job in hand. It is *not* just the adding of refinement or decoration to an already made or partly finished piece of work.

If each of the main design problems can be thought about separately, then it is unlikely that some vital point will be omitted in the final design. Fig. 354 shows how the planning of a piece of woodwork can be broken down into four main stages.

In stages 1 and 2 we ask ourselves a series of questions. The answers to these questions are used in stages 3 and 4 to enable us to solve the problems of the design as a whole.

In Fig. 354 the questions are concerned with a bathroom cupboard, but similar questions should be asked about every job which is to be made.

**Stage 1 Purpose or function of job**

Examples of questions:
What will be stored in it? How much space will be needed? How high, wide, deep will it be? Is a mirror wanted? Will it hang on the wall or stand on a shelf?

**Stage 2 Development of ideas from Stage 1**

a *Proportion* (balance in appearance)
Examples of questions:
Does the shape look right? Is it too tall for the width? Is the door frame too heavy compared with the carcase edges?

b *Materials*
Hardwood or softwood? Plywood or hardboard back? Brass or steel hinges? Ball catch or lock?

c *Construction*
Carcase corner joints: Dovetails? Housings? Fixed or adjustable shelf? How is mirror fixed? How is door knob fixed?

d *Decoration and finish*
Is there any additional surface decoration? Veneering? Carving? Shaping? Steam resistant finish needed? Clear finish to show grain of wood? Coloured finish to hide plain grain of softwood?

e *Harmony*
Is the style suitable? Does it blend in with other bathroom furniture? Does colour or grain clash with those of other nearby objects?

**Stage 3 Arrangement of ideas** (see Fig. 362)

Make short notes and dimensioned sketches of
a the complete job
b details of parts needing extra attention

**Stage 4 Working drawing** (see Fig. 367)

Completes design and planning stage

NOTE: *can you think of any more questions to ask in stages 1 and 2?*

Fig. 354

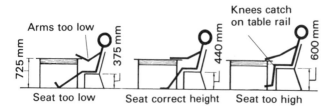

Fig. 355

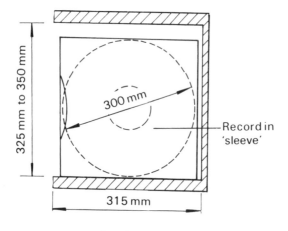

Fig. 356

## STAGE 1: JOB REQUIREMENT

'What is the *purpose* (use or function) of the finished job?' seems an easy question to answer, but for any useful progress to be made our answer must be quite detailed.

The function of any piece of work might be to store objects, to support an object or objects, to act as a working surface, and so on – or it might combine several of these functions (for example, a table fitted with a drawer).

### (a) Standard sizes

Any piece of furniture on which people will sit, or at which they will sit or stand, must be of correct size and convenient shape for the average person. For example, the seat of a dining chair should be approximately 420 mm to 440 mm high so that the sitter can sit up comfortably to the table (Fig. 355).

A working surface for a standing adult needs to be 825 mm to 900 mm high; if the adult is seated, 720 mm to 750 mm is a convenient height for writing or eating. Can you think of any other standard sizes?

### (b) Other fixed dimensions

The length, width and height of the job (or any part of it) will be determined by its particular use, whether it is a working surface or storage compartment, a lamp bracket or coal-house door. For example, the inside measurements of a record cabinet for the larger long-playing records would need to be at least 325 mm high and 315 mm deep to take the records in their 'sleeves' when stored upright (Fig. 356). The length of the cabinet would depend on the number of records to be stored.

The space between shelves in a bookcase must be sufficient to allow easy upright storage and removal of the books, but should not be excessive or space will be wasted (Fig. 357). Perhaps, in this case, adjustable shelves (as in Figs. 128 to 131) are the ideal solution.

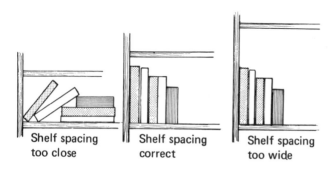

Fig. 357

## STAGE 2: DEVELOPMENT OF IDEAS

### (a) **Proportion**

Having decided on the exact function(s) of the finished job, and after considering any standard or otherwise fixed dimensions involved, thought must be given to proportion. (Proportion is the ratio or balance between length, height and width – see Fig. 358.)

'Does it *look* right?' is a good question to ask at this stage. Fig. 359 shows how the proportions of the parts of the job must also be balanced, or the job as a whole will look wrong. If the legs, rails and top of a stool are all 'too light', or 'too heavy', this can look just as wrong (Fig. 360). Either the job looks as though it will collapse under the slightest load – or it looks as though it is made for an elephant.

The solution to this problem is to use wood thick enough or wide enough to be sufficiently strong to do its work, but no thicker. Often the joints used will dictate the final dimensions of rails, stiles, legs, etc. Quite obviously the rails and legs of a workbench will need to be much heavier than those of a lady's sewing table. Often rails may be shaped and legs tapered to 'lighten' a job without weakening the joints, where adequate strength is needed (Figs. 65c and d, and 69).

Chamfers (Figs. 174a and b, and 176) and mouldings (Figs. 175 and 181a) also have this effect of 'lightening' a job by making the rails or carcase edges appear thinner than they really are.

### (b) **Materials**

The selection of particular materials for certain jobs will depend upon two main factors:

(i) the purpose or function of the finished job. (One would not use mahogany for garden fences, nor cheap grade softwoods where a highly decorative polished finish is required.)

(ii) the physical suitability of the materials. Blockboard (Fig. 255b) might be ideal for a table top but is unsuitable for use as legs or for a door frame. Solid wood is ideal for rails and so on, but is not as good as plywood if a large but light, one-piece table top is required (e.g. a table-tennis table). Waterproof grade plywood could be used in canoe building, but standard grade hardboard which is not waterproof could not.

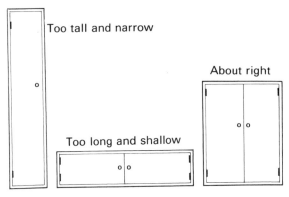

Too tall and narrow

About right

Too long and shallow

Fig. 358

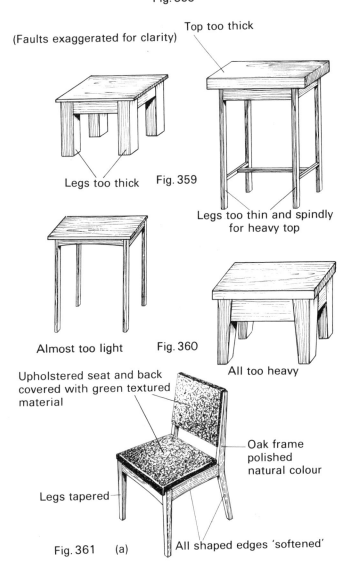

(Faults exaggerated for clarity)     Top too thick

Legs too thick     Fig. 359

Legs too thin and spindly for heavy top

Almost too light     Fig. 360

All too heavy

Upholstered seat and back covered with green textured material

Oak frame polished natural colour

Legs tapered

All shaped edges 'softened'

Fig. 361     (a)

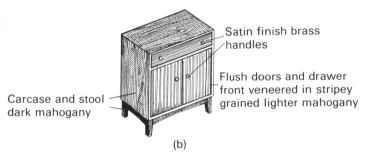

Satin finish brass handles

Flush doors and drawer front veneered in stripey grained lighter mahogany

Carcase and stool dark mahogany

(b)

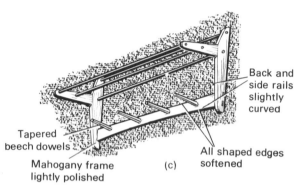

Back and side rails slightly curved

Tapered beech dowels

All shaped edges softened

Mahogany frame lightly polished

(c)

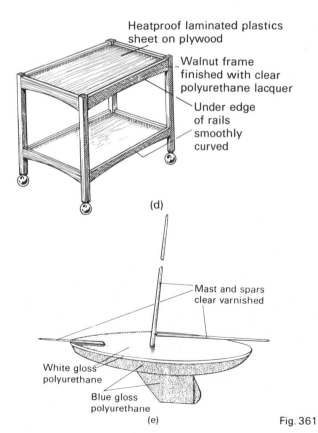

Heatproof laminated plastics sheet on plywood

Walnut frame finished with clear polyurethane lacquer

Under edge of rails smoothly curved

(d)

Mast and spars clear varnished

White gloss polyurethane

Blue gloss polyurethane

(e)                         Fig. 361

NOTE: *some useful questions to ask here are*:

*Is the job to be used inside or outside? What type of finish is to be used – transparent (clear varnish) or opaque (a coloured paint)? (This may affect the choice of wood.)*

*Are there any wide, flat surfaces involved on the job? What adhesive should be used? (See the chart on pages 54–5. If plastics or metal fittings are needed, are they strong enough – will they rust?*

*If plastics-faced boards are used, are they of the correct type for the particular job?*

### (c) Construction

The method of construction – of jointing or fixing together all the parts of the job – will depend on:

(i)  the materials used. Usually traditional (standard) joints are used for natural timber, but sometimes special techniques and adhesives are needed for manufactured boards (see Chapters 1 and 2).

(ii) the type of woodwork – cabinet-making, joinery, or rough carpentry. You might dovetail (but not nail together) the sides of a polished oak cupboard. Nailing would be satisfactory for assembling seed boxes, where dovetailing would be a waste of time and effort.

Thus the final choice of method for jointing the job will depend both upon the use of the finished article and the materials from which it is to be made.

NOTE: *look carefully at different types of woodwork and at jobs made in various materials to see how they are held together.*

### (d) Decoration and finish

Too often the appearance of otherwise well designed work is spoiled by unnecessary decoration. The smooth curves and outlines of a canoe or model yacht would be marred by adding anything other than colour, which should be used to emphasise and not to break up the natural lines of the boat, which arise from its functional shape.

If a table top is made of finely figured timber, it would generally be wrong to add too much in the way of carving, veneering, or inlay, to stain it, or in any way to detract from its pleasing natural appearance.

Methods of decorating and finishing woodwork are described in detail in Chapters 4 and 7. Chosen with care, they can add to the pleasure one gets in looking at and using such articles, whatever their size, shape and use.

Much of the best of modern woodwork depends for its decoration on good proportion and a pleasing shape, on attractively grained, lightly polished woods, or on textured and coloured surfaces. Fig. 361a to e shows examples of such work. Note how their function often dictates their shape and how this in itself is pleasing to the eye.

### (e) Harmony

However useful and attractive the finished job may be, always remember that it has to take its place alongside other things and must fit agreeably into its surroundings.

A cupboard painted bright green or yellow might look very well on the kitchen wall, but would not readily blend with a blue carpet and polished mahogany furniture in the living room. A decoratively-veneered or inlaid table would be out of place in a kitchen, where one having a laminated plastics-surfaced top would be more at home, especially when used for preparing food.

### STAGE 3: ARRANGEMENT OF IDEAS

Having found satisfactory answers to the questions we asked in stages 1 and 2, we come now to the most difficult part of the job. To use all this information is rather like putting together the parts of a jig-saw puzzle, and often we have to try out several ways of assembling it before we find the right one.

The best way of doing this is to try out our ideas in the form of sketches, adding notes where necessary to remind ourselves of important details. Fig. 362a and b shows a series of sketches and notes which arise from the points raised in Fig. 354 about a bathroom cupboard. The following suggestions will help those who find sketching difficult.

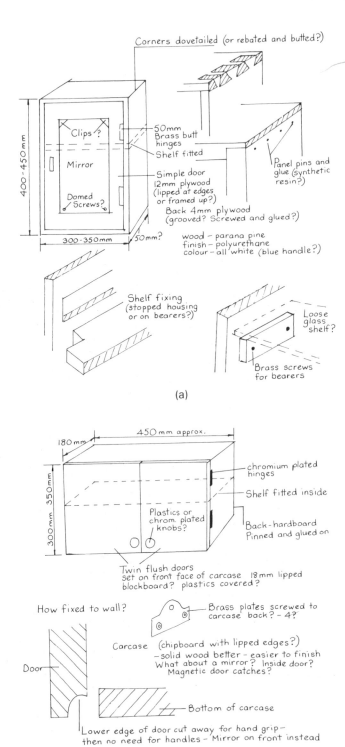

Fig. 362

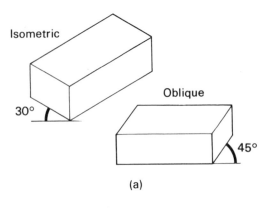

Isometric

Oblique

30°

45°

(a)

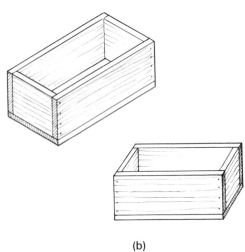

(b)

## Proportion

Most wooden objects are shaped basically like rectangular blocks, or will fit into such a block (Fig. 363a to e). Others consist of a number of smaller blocks arranged like building bricks (Fig. 364a to e). Even round or cylindrical shaped objects can be fitted in to these rectangular blocks (Fig. 365a to c).

Thus when starting your sketch, lightly outline the block (or blocks) as shown by the dotted lines in Figs. 362 to 365.

NOTE:

(*a*) *It is most important first to get the overall proportions correct.*

(*b*) *All upright lines must be kept vertical, but lines which are normally horizontal are either all tipped up about 30° – as in Isometric projection, or the front is drawn square and the end of the object tipped up about 45° – as in Oblique projection.*

(*c*) *While perspective (the apparent coming together of parallel lines as they move further from the eye) is important to the artist, we, unless we are artistically gifted, can ignore it. The object will still look real enough to be recognisable.*

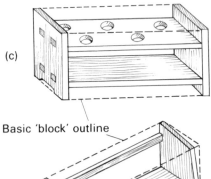

(c)

Basic 'block' outline

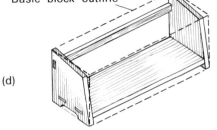

(d)

(e)

Fig. 363

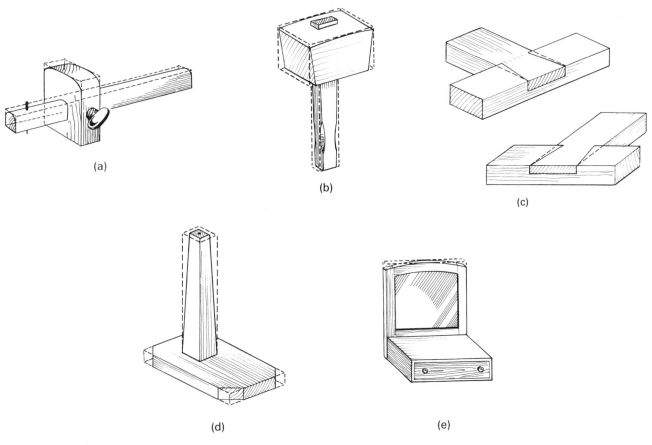

(a)

(b)

(c)

(d)

(e)

Fig. 364

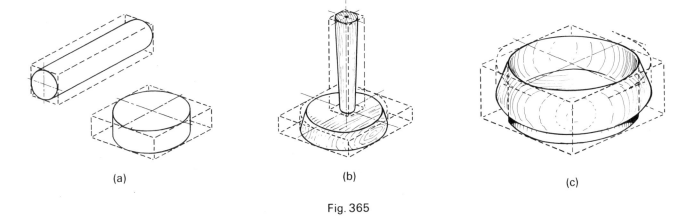

(a)

(b)

(c)

Fig. 365

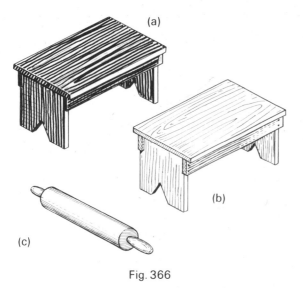

(a)

(b)

(c)

Fig. 366

## Shading

Do not try to make your sketches look realistic by shading heavily (Fig. 366a). Indicate the end grain and add a *few* lines to show the direction of the grain as in Fig. 366b.

In Fig. 366c, shadow is suggested to emphasise the curved surfaces, but again this should not be done if the attempt results in heavy pencil shading.

## STAGE 4: THE WORKING DRAWING

With simple jobs it is often possible to work successfully from the notes and sketches produced in Stage 3, but larger, more complicated pieces of woodwork need to be accurately drawn out as working drawings.

Working drawings enable us to see every detail of the job. We can, by reading the drawing, ensure that each part is made in the right way to the right size.

Fig. 367 shows a working drawing or *Orthographic projection* made from the sketches and notes given in Fig. 362. Note how, instead of a pictorial view of the whole cupboard, we are given accurate *separate* views of its front, side and top which are drawn out either full size or to scale.

Hidden details are often shown by dotted lines (Fig. 368), or where necessary by section or part section views as in Fig. 369a and b. Fig. 370 shows the different types of line commonly used in working drawings. Dimensions are inserted where required as in Figs. 367 and 371. The letter R in front of a number indicates that the dimension is a radius; the symbol ∅ in front of a number indicates a diameter. All dimensions are positioned so that they can be read from the *bottom* or *right side* of the drawing. NOTE: *it is not possible to explain all the details of Orthographic projection in this short chapter. Its purpose is to show why such drawings are necessary, how they form a part of designing and planning, and to give a brief account of what is involved in making and reading them.*

From the working drawing (Figs. 367 to 369), a cutting list can be prepared as in Fig. 78.

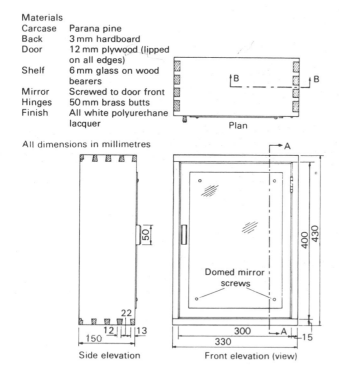

Materials
Carcase    Parana pine
Back       3 mm hardboard
Door       12 mm plywood (lipped
           on all edges)
Shelf      6 mm glass on wood
           bearers
Mirror     Screwed to door front
Hinges     50 mm brass butts
Finish     All white polyurethane
           lacquer

All dimensions in millimetres

Plan

Side elevation

Front elevation (view)

Domed mirror screws

Fig. 367 (third angle projection)

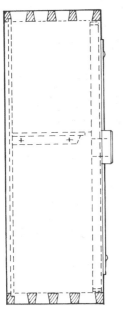

Side elevation showing hidden detail
Fig. 368

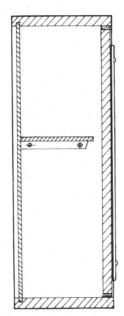

(a) Sectional side elevation on A–A

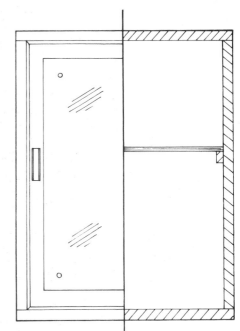

(b) Front elevation with half sectional elevation on B–B

Fig. 369

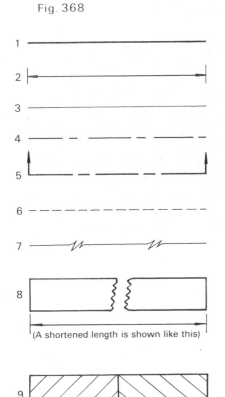

(A shortened length is shown like this)

Fig. 370

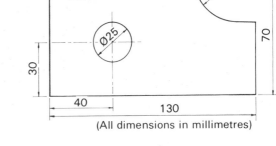

(All dimensions in millimetres)

Key to Fig. 370          Fig. 371

1 Outlines: bold
2 Dimension lines: thinner than outlines, with closed arrow heads
3 Construction lines: very faint
4 Centre lines
5 Section lines
6 Hidden details
7 and 8  Break lines
9 Section shading (cross hatching) – shade adjoining pieces in different directions

# 12 Projects

A *practical project* usually takes one of two forms – it is either a piece of woodwork decided upon by a student or group of students, and designed and made during a part or the whole of the school year, or a piece of woodwork selected from a list set by an examination board. (Again a student designs and makes up his chosen model, usually taking one or two terms to complete it, although some boards allow a shorter time to complete a simpler job. This 'short project' sometimes replaces the practical test in the woodwork examination.)

A *personal study* is a piece of research into a chosen branch of woodworking or into some aspect of the craft which is of particular interest to the student. This study when completed often takes the form of a folder containing notes, sketches, and photographs, etc., and may be related to the practical coursework mentioned in the previous paragraph.

A study of boat-building might, for example, lead to the making of a model racing yacht or catamaran, a canoe, or even a sailing dinghy. An interest in musical instruments could result in the making of a Spanish or electric guitar; research into steam bending or laminating naturally leads to the production of hockey sticks, sledges, skis, bentwood furniture, and so on.

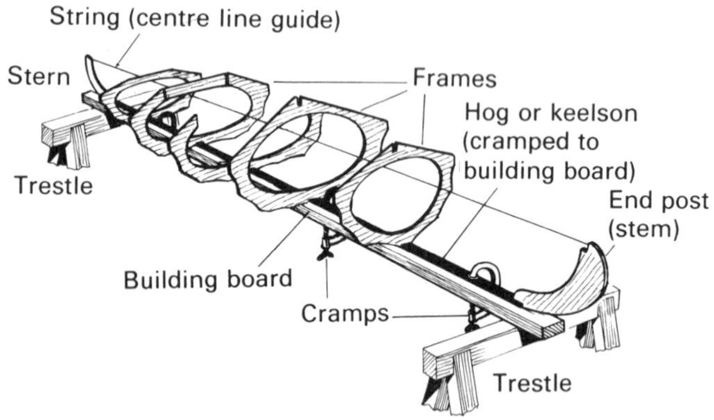

Fig. 372

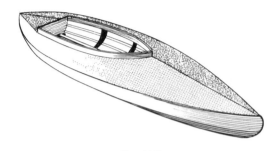

String (centre line guide)

Stern

Frames

Hog or keelson
(cramped to
building board)

Trestle

End post
(stem)

Building board

Cramps

Trestle

(a)

Fig. 373

## PRACTICAL PROJECTS

The type, the arrangement, and the details of the project or coursework undertaken will vary a great deal, but the following notes and suggestions may be of use to all students. The notes cover a wide range of craft topics. Some sources of additional information are given, and suggestions made for ways of setting about the practical work and preparing personal study folders.

## Boats and canoes

### Fabric-covered

This popular type of canoe is wooden-framed
and canvas-covered (Fig. 372). The framework is
made by screwing and gluing wooden 'stringers'
(strips of softwood), usually of about 38 mm ×
12 mm section, to a series of plywood frames.

(a) The frames and end posts are cut from 10 mm
thick marine (waterproof) grade plywood.
Full-sized drawings of these parts may be
purchased, and in some canoe kits the frames are
already sawn out. All sharp edges must be
removed before assembly.

(b) The end posts and frames are glued and screwed
to the 'hog' (a straight inner keel), and this is
cramped or screwed to a heavier building board
which holds the frames and hog true while the
first stringers and other parts are added. The
centre line through the canoe must be kept dead
straight or the finished boat will not handle
properly. String stretched between the tops of
the end posts will act as a useful guide (Fig.
373a).

(c) The gunwales (heavier stringers forming the top
outer edges of the canoe) are then fitted, starting
from the centre frames and working towards the
end posts.

(d) The cockpit coaming frames and the stringers
are then added, and their ends tapered so as to
fit snugly to the end posts.

(e) The canoe framework may be taken off the
building board and turned upside down to fit the
lower stringers, as once the gunwales and side
stringers have been fitted the framework is
unlikely to twist (Fig. 373b).

(f) When all stringers and additional wooden parts
have been fitted, the whole skeleton should be
well glasspapered and all sharp edges removed
(Fig. 373c). Several coats of clear varnish should
then be applied. The keel and rubbing strips
should be prepared and 'offered up' to the canoe,
but not actually fitted until the framework has
been covered.

(g) With the framework upside down, the covering
fabric – canvas or PVC – is correctly positioned
and fitted, using copper tacks. Tack the stretched

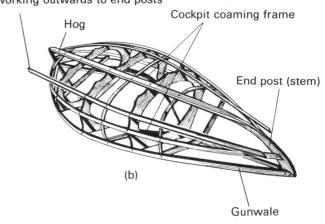

Stringers are screwed to frames,
starting from the centre and
working outwards to end posts

Hog

Cockpit coaming frame

End post (stem)

(b)

Gunwale

Fig. 373 (b)

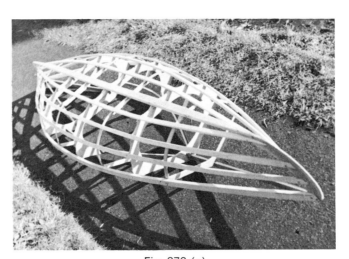

Fig. 373 (c)

fabric to each end post and along the centre line of the hog. Turn the canoe the right way up and, working from the centre of each side, stretch the fabric tightly to avoid creases or puckering, and tack off on the inside of the gunwales.

Extra care will be needed at each end where the fabric will have to be trimmed, overlapped, glued, and tacked round the end posts.

(h) Surplus fabric is trimmed away and the keel and bilge keels are screwed on from the inside before the deck fabric is fitted. Finally, all the external woodwork and metal trim is fitted and the whole painted and/or varnished as required.

(i) Seats, bottom-boards, paddles, and so on are prepared from suitable timbers, varnished and fitted.

NOTE: *these instructions are for general guidance only. Before attempting to construct such a canoe, careful study some of the books suggested on page 149 is recommended, and accurate drawings and detailed instructions should be obtained. Consider, too, the amount of time and money involved in such a venture. Finally, before you try out your canoe, be sure you can swim!*

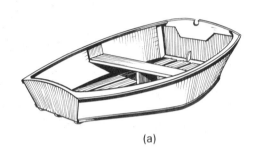

(a)

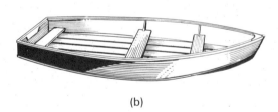

(b)

Fig. 374

## Plywood-covered

The construction of simple plywood-covered canoes and dinghies is basically similar to the methods used for fabric-covered boats. Because plywood will not easily bend in two directions at the same time, such boats tend to be 'slab-sided'. However, less internal framing is necessary because the plywood skin itself adds a great deal of stiffness and strength to the boat as a whole.

The shape of plywood-covered boats varies considerably. The 'pram' dinghy (Fig. 374a), which is the smallest type worth making, is rather punt-shaped, while the 'stem' dinghy (Fig. 374b) has a pointed bow and square stern. Where sea-going or fast sailing craft are required, more complex hull shapes are needed.

## Clinker and carvel built

These boats use solid timber for the skin and require considerable skill to construct. The techniques involved are outside the scope of this book, as are those needed for the production of glass-fibre hulls.

*Books and sources of information*
P. W. Blandford    *Canoes and Canoeing*
    Lutterworth Press, 1962
P. W. Blandford    *Small Boats and Sailing*
    Lutterworth Press, 1963
P. W. Blandford    *Build Your Own Boat*
    Stanley Paul, 1966
*Light Craft* (monthly)
The Secretary, British Canoe Union, 26 Park
    Crescent, London W1

## Carving and treenwork
Although not constructional woodwork, carving and treenwork offer wide scope for students interested in form, shape and texture. Even simple work can be very attractive when neatly finished, and some of it can be useful too (see Chapter 5).

*Books and sources of information*
A. Durst    *Wood Carving*    Studio Vista, 1959
C. Graveney    *Woodcarving for Beginners*    Studio
    Vista, 1967
P. E. Norman    *Sculpture in Wood*    Tiranti, 1962
W. T. James    *Treen: a book of gougework*    Pitman,
    1950
E. H. Pinto    *Treen and other Wooden Bygones*
    Bell, 1969    (A magnificent book of over 700
    pages, with many illustrations, to consult in a
    library.)
E. Rottger    *Creative Wood Craft*    Batsford, 1961.

*Look out for*: church woodwork and antique furniture; some of the small animal carvings imported from Africa; exhibits in certain art galleries and museums.

## Country woodcrafts (coppice work)
Many country woodcrafts have died out or are fading away because of lack of demand. The village wheel-wright, the clogmaker, the basket maker, the rake-maker and even the thatcher have all but disappeared from the country scene, though some of their products and the methods employed in making them are still of use and interest today.

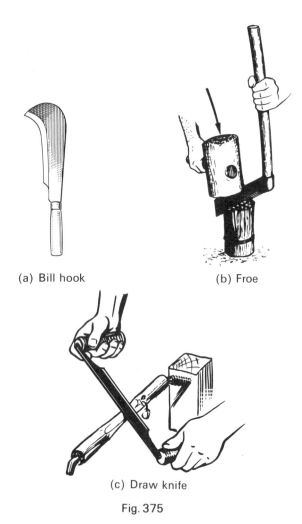

(a) Bill hook          (b) Froe

(c) Draw knife

Fig. 375

These craftsmen really understood the timbers they used and, often using very simple tools and equipment, produced useful articles perfectly suited to the work for which they were designed.

Many of these articles can be made from coppice-wood – that is, light branches, poles and trimmings cut from willow, hazel, ash, and sweet-chestnut trees. (Examples are shown in Fig. 375d.) Often these trees are cut down close to the ground, and from the stumps grow the light and fairly straight stems which are harvested every five to fifteen years.

If the pole is too thick for its purpose, it is split, not sawn, to size. This ensures that the grain runs straight all the way along it, avoiding weakness through short or cross grain.

Poles are split through the heart (centre) with an axe, bill hook (Fig. 375a), or 'froe' (Fig. 375b), and then sliced to thickness and trued to shape with a draw-knife (Fig. 375c). Often a 'shaving-horse' (Fig. 376) is used to hold and support the wood being worked.

Where prepared wood needs softening before being bent to shape, it is boiled or steamed (see Chapter 3).

Two useful pieces of equipment, well worth making, are the 'rounder', for rounding and pointing the ends of poles, ladder-staves, and so on (Fig. 377), and the 'stail engine', a somewhat similar tool used for making long tapers, round handles, and such items. In each case the work is held firmly and the tool revolved round it rather like a rotating spokeshave.

For details of the methods used in the making of coppice products, reference should be made to the books listed below.

*Books and other sources of information*

J. G. Jenkins    *Traditional Country Craftsmen*
    Routledge & Kegan Paul, 1965
F. Lambert    *Tools and Devices for Coppice Crafts*
    Evans Bros., Young Farmers' Clubs series, 1958
The Rural Industries Bureau, 35 Camp Road,
    Wimbledon, London SW19

*Look out for*: any local craftsmen still carrying on country woodcrafts.

Fig. 375 (d)

## Furniture: Domestic furniture

The common forms of furniture, furniture design, construction and decoration have been dealt with in previous chapters.

Many students produce simple stools, coffee tables, boxes, and small cupboards, but these are often copied from existing pieces. Why not read Chapter 11 again and design your own piece of furniture entirely by yourself? Here is a list of useful items.

### Tables

Coffee tables – long, square, round oval (Figs. 65b, c, e, f, and 66); barrel-shaped; kidney-shaped; low (300 mm) to high (600 mm)
Nests of tables (one fitting inside another)
Bedside tables (with or without a drawer)
Folding card tables
Kitchen tables, plastics-topped
Television tables
Hall tables
Chess or draughts tables, with veneered chequer-board top
Telephone tables (would a bracketed shelf be as useful?)
Side tables (need to be as high as a dining table – 725 mm – and are usually fitted with a cutlery drawer)
Dining tables – only for the very ambitious!

### Stools

High kitchen stools – with wooden top (Fig. 123), padded top (Fig. 65d), woven top (Figs. 65 and 127e)
Music stool with lift-up lid
Foot stool

### Cupboards (Figs. 92b and 94)

Shoe, bookcase, kitchen (Fig. 93), bathroom (Fig. 367), medicine, fitted (built-in), record cabinet (Fig. 356), hall (Fig. 360b), china display cabinet

### Boxes

Shoe-cleaning materials and brushes
Games (draughts, chess, etc.)
Hobbies (stamps, coins, photographs, etc.)

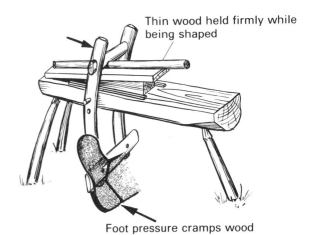

Thin wood held firmly while being shaped

Foot pressure cramps wood

Fig. 376 Shaving horse

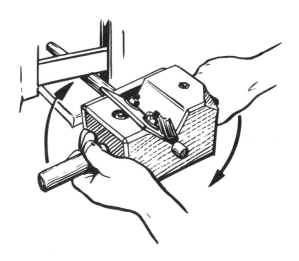

Fig. 377 Rounder

Tools (modelling, cycle kit)
Cutlery case

**Miscellaneous items**
Clothes horse
Book racks (Fig. 173)
Tea trolley (Fig. 361d)
Chair (Fig. 361a)
Clothes rack (Fig. 361c)

Furniture can be made in the traditional way with dovetails, mortice and tenon joints, and so on; alternatively, simpler constructions are possible using chipboard, blockboard, and other new materials and modern adhesives. (See Chapters 1, 2 and 3.)

NOTE: *before attempting any large piece of furniture, be sure you will have enough time in which to complete it.*

*Books and sources of information*
F. J. and R. B. Christopher    *The ABC of Furniture Making*    Faber, 1957
S. H. Glenister    *Contemporary Design in Woodwork* (3 vols)    Murray, 1955, 1961, 1968
C. H. Hayward    *Cabinet Making for Beginners* Evans Bros., 1963
*Ideal Home* (monthly); *House and Garden* (monthly); *Practical Householder* (monthly); *Woodworker* (monthly); *Practical Woodworking* (monthly)
*Look out for*: furniture shops and showrooms, furniture exhibitions (in all of which you can probably collect catalogues).

**Furniture: Garden and camping furniture**
Furniture used out of doors, both in the garden and when camping, has to be designed and made to withstand the weather. Rain, strong sunlight, and ice would soon spoil most indoor furniture, but several outdoor pieces can be made without too much difficulty (Figs. 378 to 380).

(a)  Teak or afrormosia

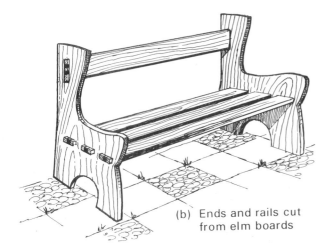

(b)  Ends and rails cut
from elm boards

Fig. 378

Fig. 379 Made of durable hardwood. Joints pegged or
glued using waterproof adhesive

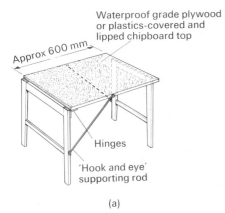

Waterproof grade plywood
or plastics-covered and
lipped chipboard top

Approx 600 mm

Hinges

'Hook and eye'
supporting rod

(a)

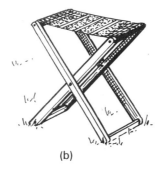

(b)

(c)

Fig. 380

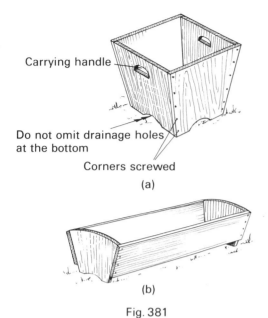

Carrying handle

Do not omit drainage holes at the bottom

Corners screwed

(a)

(b)

Fig. 381

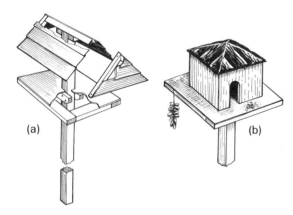

Corners screwed or dovetailed

Front faced with varnished split silver birch poles (with bark) or moulded western red cedar

Fig. 382

## Garden woodwork

Many useful wooden articles may be made for the garden and around the house. Plant tubs, window boxes and bird-tables (Figs. 381 to 383) are easily constructed, and when painted or treated with a suitable preservative will give years of useful service.

Wheelbarrows need not be of the traditional shape. A smaller, two-wheeled version (Fig. 384), using two old pram wheels, is very useful for collecting leaves and garden refuse.

All keen gardeners need a cold frame such as that illustrated in Fig. 43a. Fig. 385 shows a simple method of constructing the base, and Figs. 386 and 387 indicate ways of making the 'lights' (sliding frames). It is not necessary to use glass; some of the new reinforced clear plastics are lighter in weight and less easily broken.

NOTE: *in all cases check on available sizes of glass or plastics sheet before starting, so as to use these materials economically.*

*Because cold frames tend to retain a great deal of moisture, it is a good idea to give all joints a thick coat of priming paint and assemble them while the paint is still wet. This will help to keep out water and thus prevent rotting.*

It might be possible for a group to make a greenhouse.

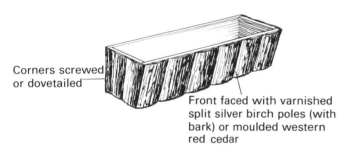

(a)

(b)

Fig. 383

Fig. 384

## Garden gates

Many gates are patched up and repaired when they might well be replaced with new ones. Fig. 388a to e shows possible ways of making them.

First decide:

(a) the actual size of gate (allow for the hinges and clearance when measuring the gap between the gate posts);

(b) how heavy a gate is required; and

(c) whether the gate is to be chiefly ornamental or practical (does it have to keep a dog from getting loose?).

Variations in shape and detail can be made once the overall dimensions have been established.

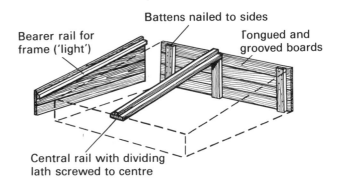

Bearer rail for frame ('light')

Battens nailed to sides

Tongued and grooved boards

Central rail with dividing lath screwed to centre

Fig. 385

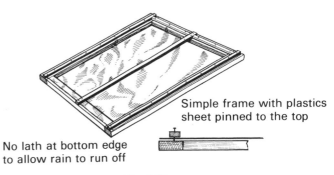

Simple frame with plastics sheet pinned to the top

No lath at bottom edge to allow rain to run off

Fig. 387

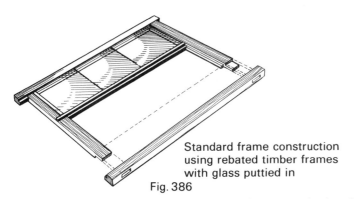

Standard frame construction using rebated timber frames with glass puttied in

Fig. 386

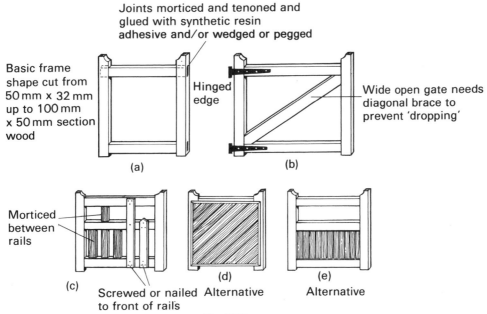

Joints morticed and tenoned and glued with synthetic resin adhesive and/or wedged or pegged

Basic frame shape cut from 50 mm x 32 mm up to 100 mm x 50 mm section wood

Hinged edge

Wide open gate needs diagonal brace to prevent 'dropping'

(a)  (b)

Morticed between rails

Screwed or nailed to front of rails

(c)  (d)  Alternative  (e)  Alternative

Fig. 388

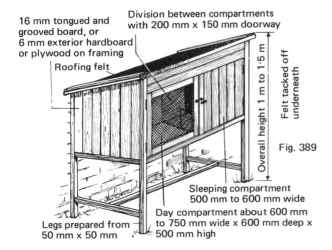

16 mm tongued and grooved board, or 6 mm exterior hardboard or plywood on framing

Roofing felt

Division between compartments with 200 mm × 150 mm doorway

Overall height 1 m to 1·5 m

Felt tacked off underneath

Fig. 389

Sleeping compartment 500 mm to 600 mm wide

Day compartment about 600 mm to 750 mm wide × 600 mm deep × 500 mm high

Legs prepared from 50 mm × 50 mm

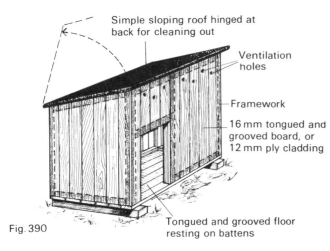

Simple sloping roof hinged at back for cleaning out

Ventilation holes

Framework

16 mm tongued and grooved board, or 12 mm ply cladding

Fig. 390

Tongued and grooved floor resting on battens

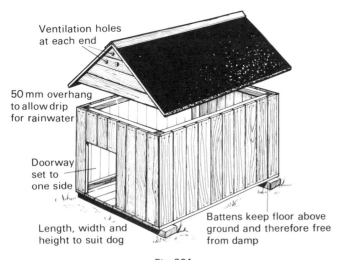

Ventilation holes at each end

50 mm overhang to allow drip for rainwater

Doorway set to one side

Length, width and height to suit dog

Battens keep floor above ground and therefore free from damp

Fig. 391

## Rabbit hutches and dog kennels

Sometimes rabbits, dogs and other pets are housed out of doors in converted packing cases and fruit boxes. These are often cold, draughty and unhygienic, and if your pet has such a home he should be rehoused. Here are a few ideas that may help in designing a suitable hutch or kennel.

Fig. 389 shows a hutch. If 16 mm tongued and grooved boards are used throughout, this will ensure that the hutch remains warm enough during the winter yet does not get too hot during the summer. A loose-fitting shutter may be used to cover the wire mesh door during very bad weather. This shutter could be of solid timber, plywood, or hardboard, or a sheet of framed clear plastics material such as heavy quality polythene. When the roof has been covered with roofing felt, the inside should be lime-washed and the outside creosoted or painted.

Figs. 390 and 391 illustrate two types of dog kennel. The size of a dog kennel must suit its occupant – be sure to allow room inside for your pet to turn round and stretch his legs in comfort. Allow enough headroom, too, or the kennel may become unbearably hot and stuffy during the summer months. Remember that what at first may be a small puppy may well grow to be a very large dog in quite a short time, so find out how big your dog is likely to become before designing his kennel.

*Sources of information*

Various do-it-yourself and gardening magazines. *Look out for*: garden supply shops and public parks and gardens.

## Musical instruments

A number of worth-while instruments can be made without involving any difficult woodworking. Many boys enjoy playing guitars (Spanish or electric), but if these are thought too difficult to make, the simpler lyres, chordal dulcimers, and zithers (see Fig. 392a) are well worth attempting.

Unlike guitars, these simple instruments have no frets for altering the pitch (raising or lowering the notes). Instead, each string produces one note only – rather like a harp. The size and shape of these stringed instruments varies considerably, but the construction of all of them is basically the same.

(a) The sides, made from any suitable close-grained hardwood, are simply jointed, pinned and glued together (Fig. 392b).

(b) The top and bottom, of 4 mm plywood, are then glued on to the sides with synthetic resin glue, and cramped evenly round the edges until the adhesive is completely set (Fig. 392c). (Bore out the sound hole before gluing the top to the sides.)

(c) The surplus plywood is trimmed away and the 'box' cleaned up.

(d) The bridge (or bridges) is (are) glued into position and the whole box varnished or treated with a wood sealer.

(e) 'Hitch' pins, 'wrest' pins, and strings are added, and the instrument is then ready to be tuned and played.

NOTE: *groups can have a great deal of fun with these instruments; they can be made quite cheaply and produce a sound which is as pleasant, if not quite so loud, as that of professionally-made guitars.*

For further information on the making of these instruments, xylophones, bamboo pipes and recorders, see the books listed below.

*Books and sources of information*

M. Galloway   *Making and Playing Bamboo Pipes*
   Dryad Press, 1967
M. Mandell   *Make Your Own Musical Instruments*
   Bailey Bros., 1970
R. Roberts   *Musical Instruments made to be Played*
   Dryad Press, 1965

*Materials* from Messrs Mickleburgh, Stokes Croft, Bristol

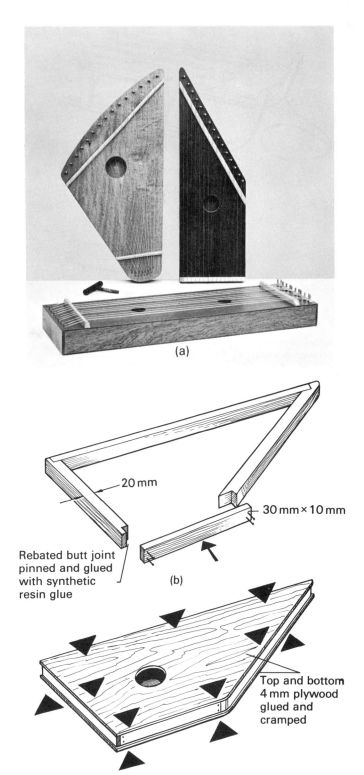

(a)

20 mm

30 mm × 10 mm

Rebated butt joint pinned and glued with synthetic resin glue

(b)

Top and bottom 4 mm plywood glued and cramped

Fig. 392

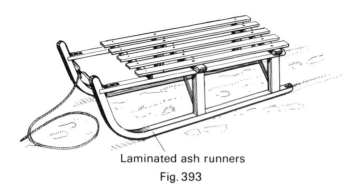

Laminated ash runners

Fig. 393

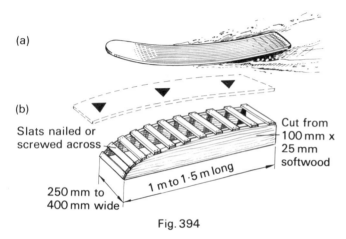

(a)

(b)

Slats nailed or
screwed across

Cut from
100 mm x
25 mm
softwood

1 m to 1·5 m long

250 mm to
400 mm wide

Fig. 394

(a)

1·5 m to 2·5 m

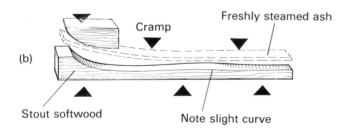

Cramp

Freshly steamed ash

(b)

Stout softwood

Note slight curve

Fig. 395

## Sports equipment

Laminating and steam bending, described in
Chapter 3, may be used in making several useful
and quite exciting pieces of sports equipment.

## Sledges

As already described (page 41), sledge runners can
be laminated from ash. After cleaning up, they can
be jointed to form a strong but simple frame, and
fitted with a slatted top (Fig. 393). Thin steel or
brass strip should be screwed carefully to the
underside of the runners and the whole sledge given
several coats of varnish or polyurethane lacquer.

## Surfboards

The size and shape of surfboards varies considerably,
but a simple board (Fig. 394a) can be made by
cramping three or four thicknesses of 2 mm or 3 mm
waterproof grade plywood over a jig or former (Fig.
394b), coating their mating surfaces with synthetic
resin glue.

It is possible to make more advanced 'double
skinned' (hollow) surfboards, and working drawings
for such boards are available.

Once the adhesive has set, the edges should be
trued up and well rounded to ensure that there are
no splinters or sharp edges which could cut or
scratch the surfer. The board should be thoroughly
painted or varnished before use.

## Skis

Provided that the special metal boot clamps can be
bought or made in the school workshop, the skis
themselves (Fig. 395a) can be made by shaping and
steaming straight grained ash or hickory and
cramping it to a correctly-shaped jig until dry.

One method is to borrow a ski and make the jig to
match the shape of its sole (underside) exactly. A
second block should be shaped to fit the inside curve
of the ski front, and the freshly steamed timber can
then be cramped firmly in place until dry (Fig.
395b).

NOTE: *some shaping and tapering of the ski body is
necessary, and a shallow groove should run along the
underside of the ski sole. This work should be carried
out BEFORE the ski is steamed to shape.*

*Laminated skis are another possibility, but care must be taken to ensure that the laminates are very tightly glued together throughout their length. Thick glue lines must be avoided.*

## Archery equipment

### Bowmaking

Suitable lengths of yew, the wood traditionally used for the making of longbows, are now rarely available, but degame (sometimes called lemonwood or lancewood) is a satisfactory substitute. This timber can be obtained from specialist suppliers.

Solid wooden bows are fairly easy to make provided that care is taken to ensure that the tapering is even.

(a) Set out a 1·65 m to 1·85 m length of 25 mm square wood as in Fig. 396a. Note that the upper arm is 50 mm longer than the lower, and that the front-back tapering is all carried out from the 'belly' side (the side facing the bow string).

(b) Mark out the sides and taper them equally. This tapering *must* be even and a centre line drawn on in pencil will help to ensure this (Fig. 396b).

(c) Round the sharp edges until the various cross-sections are as shown in Fig. 396c. Note that the belly side of the bow is well rounded while the 'back' (the side away from the string) is nearly flat.

(d) Glue on a thin strip of wood at X and complete the shaping of the handle. The handle may be covered by gluing round a piece of thin leather, or by binding with stout string (Fig. 396d).

(e) Cut the notches (Fig. 396e) and fit the bow string. 'Tillering' the bow consists of bending it and adjusting it with a plane or spokeshave until a smooth curve is obtained. Too much bending in one part is relieved by removing a *little* wood on either side of it until a smooth curve is obtained when the bow is fully bent.

(f) Remove the string, and glasspaper the bow until a very fine, smooth surface is obtained. Varnish lightly and flat down with fine glasspaper to give a satin finish.

Fig. 396

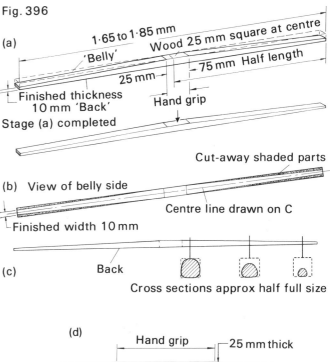

(a) 1·65 to 1·85 mm  'Belly'  Wood 25 mm square at centre  25 mm  75 mm Half length  Finished thickness 10 mm 'Back'  Hand grip  Stage (a) completed

Cut-away shaded parts

(b) View of belly side  Centre line drawn on C  Finished width 10 mm

(c) Back  Cross sections approx half full size

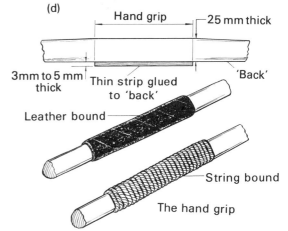

(d) Hand grip  25 mm thick  3mm to 5 mm thick  Thin strip glued to 'back'  'Back'  Leather bound  String bound  The hand grip

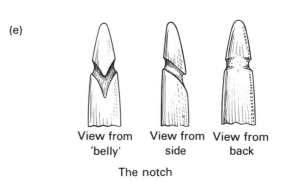

(e) View from 'belly'  View from side  View from back

The notch

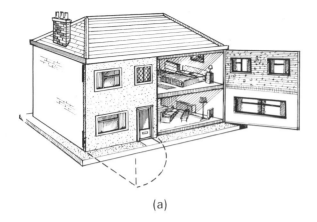

(a)

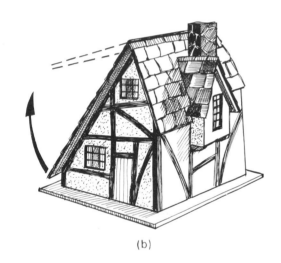

(b)

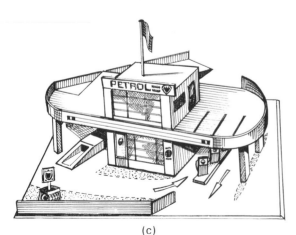

(c)

Fig. 397

**The flat bow** This is a more powerful version of the solid bow, and requires a little more skill in the making.

**Composite or laminated bows** These use a variety of woods sometimes combined with glass-fibre; they are more powerful and have a greater range than solid bows. For making them, refer to specialist literature.

**Arrows**

Arrows may be made from 8 mm birch dowel, and are usually 650 mm to 700 mm long. As 'fletching' (fitting the tail feathers) is a rather specialised job, reference books should be consulted. 'Piles' (arrow heads) may be made in the metalwork shop. Much can be learnt by studying a professionally-made arrow.

*Books and other sources of information*
E. H. Burke   *Archery*   Arco, 1969
Patrick Clover   *The Bowman's Handbook*   Patrick Clover, 27 The Dale, Widley, Portsmouth, 1968
E. G. Heath   *Archery – the Modern Approach*   Faber, 1966
T. Jennings and D. Kittredge   *How to make Bows* Sportsman Publications, Box 598, Mammoth Lakes, California, USA, 1966
*Archery materials and equipment* from D. G. Quick, 5A Arundel Street, Portsmouth, Hants., and Marksman Archery Products, Cuckney, Mansfield, Notts.

## Wooden toys

The construction of wooden toys may be as simple or as involved as the maker wishes. The sides of a toy truck, for example, might be just nailed together, or screwed and glued, or could be dovetailed. Younger brothers and sisters, and many less fortunate children in foster homes and orphanages, can have hours of fun with some of the toys suggested below.

## Dolls' houses

These may be in many sizes and styles (Fig. 397a, b and c), but provided that the front wall – or one side of the roof – is hinged, then there is no limitation on layout or finish.

Most parts are made from hardboard or plywood of various thicknesses, the rest being cut from offcuts of softwood. Walls can be 'rough-cast' – stippled with plaster of Paris or commercial filler and then painted – or covered with brick-patterned paper. Roofs can be 'tiled' with patterned paper also; it can be bought at hobbies shops.

## Desks

Fig. 398a and b shows plain desks, and Fig. 398c a decorated desk suitable for a very young child. Before starting work – measure the child! Be sure to allow enough knee room under the desk (see Fig. 355), and allow a little extra for growth.

Construction may be with conventional legs and rails using plywood for the desk lid and bottom, or all ply, blockboard, or lipped chipboard. Plywood is used for the shaped desk sides in Fig. 398c.

## Wagons and trucks

Basically these (Fig. 399a and b) are boxes on wheels, from which a whole range of toys can be made. In addition to the trucks illustrated, model engines and cars are popular.

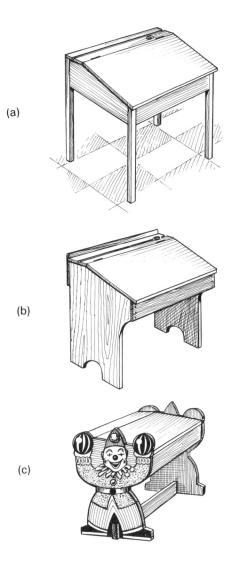

(a)

(b)

(c)

Fig. 398

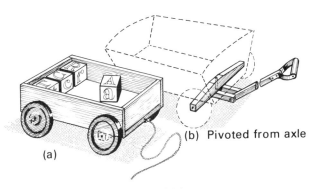

(b) Pivoted from axle

(a)

Fig. 399

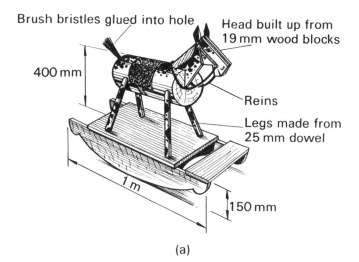

Brush bristles glued into hole

Head built up from 19 mm wood blocks

400 mm

Reins

Legs made from 25 mm dowel

1 m

150 mm

(a)

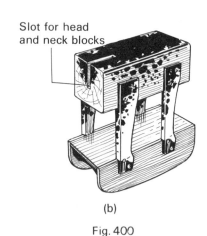

Slot for head and neck blocks

(b)

Fig. 400

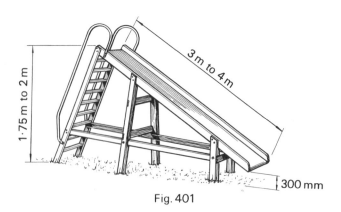

3 m to 4 m

1·75 m to 2 m

300 mm

Fig. 401

## Rocking horse

The traditional rocking horse is finely carved and very skilfully made, but a simple 'rocker' made as in Fig. 400a or b will always meet with approval.

## Garden slide

The chute of the garden slide shown in Fig. 401 may be made either from 12 mm waterproof grade plywood or (suitably braced) from 16 mm or 19 mm Parana pine. The underframe and steps can be made up in several ways depending on the availability of timber.

Such a slide is best designed so that it can be dismantled into three sections for winter storage:

(a) the underframe (bolted together);

(b) the steps;

(c) the chute.

*Books and sources of information*
K. Hils   *The Toy*   E. Ward, 1959
E. Rottger   *Creative Wood Craft*   Batsford, 1961

## Model boats and ships

The making of working models of yachts, motor boats, catamarans and ocean-going ships calls for more than mere woodworking skill.

To get the best out of a large model yacht requires a knowledge of basic sailing techniques so that adequate control may be kept over the boat's performance, and a high speed diesel-powered model motor boat needs some mechanical maintenance.

There are several ways of building hulls, and Fig. 402a to c shows three of the most common methods.

Fig. 402a (brick fashion) is usually used only for large model sailing boats. The method gives strength and yet saves a great deal of gouging away of surplus wood. Each section must be well fitted and glued to the adjoining pieces with a synthetic resin glue.

Fig. 402b shows a simple slab-sided construction often used for model motor boats. Thin waterproof grade plywood reinforced at the edges and corner joints is an ideal material for use with this construction, being light, easy to bend to shape, and yet very strong. The construction of more complex hulls for high speed boats is possible using this method.

The hulls of models of old sailing ships, galleons, and so on are often carved from solid blocks or slabs of wood. To simplify shaping, large hulls can be built up by gluing together a number of thinner partially-shaped blocks. Fig. 402c shows how a model galleon hull can be made from five blocks of wood.

Making sails, rigging, masts and so on calls for considerable patience, but much detailed guidance may be obtained from some of the specialist books listed below.

*Books and sources of information*
R. K. Battson  *Period Ship Modelling*  Model and
    Allied Publications, 1949
E. Bowness  *Modelling the 'Cutty Sark'*  Model
    and Allied Publications, 1959
R. H. Warring  *Model Power Boats*  Arco, 1964
B. W. Bathe  *Ship Models* (4 booklets, also as one
    volume)  HMSO, 1966
Also see yachting magazines.

*Look out for*: maritime museums, shipping offices, and boat building yards.

## Wood technology
Timber structures and their testing is a wide topic with many possibilities (see under Personal Study).

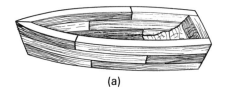

(a)

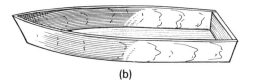

(b)

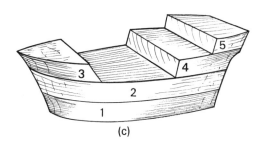

(c)

Fig. 402

## THE PERSONAL STUDY

The personal study for Secondary School examinations usually consist of (1) *finding out* about a specially chosen topic; (2) *sorting out* the information which has been obtained and using this new knowledge; and (3) *making a report* on what has been discovered.

### Finding out – sources of information

Quite often the most difficult part of the personal study is in getting started. First choose a subject in which you are interested. (There is a selection of topics on pages 165–8.) The sources of information will vary with the topic – several are listed elsewhere in this chapter, but in general there are two main ways of obtaining your facts.

### Written information:

(a) Libraries    Use your school and local libraries. The county or municipal librarian can often obtain specialist books for you if they are not part of the regular stock.

(b) Manufacturers, trade associations and government organisations    Write to manufacturers or to the secretary of any society associated with your topic. Provided that your letter is courteous and explains clearly what information is required, you will generally receive a useful reply, copies of trade literature, catalogues or special reports, and so on, which are often of considerable value.

(c) Magazines    Articles in magazines are often a good source of information, as their authors have specialised knowledge of the topic described. Write to the editor of the magazine, who will usually either put you in touch with the author, or answer your question privately or on the 'Any Questions?' page. Do not forget to send a stamped addressed envelope with your enquiry.

### Visits:

(a) Arrangements can often be made for visits to shops, churches, museums, or other buildings to examine anything of particular interest.

(b) Personal contact may be made with a local craftsman who will demonstrate his particular craft to you, and provided you show sufficient interest will explain how and why he works in his own particular way.

(c) Visits to factories, boat yards, forestry centres and other places may also be made, but remember that arrangements need to be made well in advance.

### Sorting out

Your search for information may well, after a time, leave you with an assortment of notes, jottings, sketches, catalogues, photographs and specimens. Such a jumbled mass of material does not in itself make up a report, but a report can be made by careful selection from and arrangement of it.

Here are some suggestions to guide you at this stage.

(a) Break down the subject into a number of smaller topics. List them just as you think of them and then rearrange them into the best possible order.

NOTE: *in some cases this topic analysis is best carried out BEFORE you start collecting your material, as it often helps you to make clear in your own mind exactly WHAT your aim is, and HOW you are going to tackle it.*

(b) Under each topic (or sub-topic) heading, make short notes of your own and list any reference material, photographs, specimens, etc., relevant to that section. In this way the information may be grouped and sorted into a more useful form.

(c) Once the subject-matter has been sifted and arranged as suggested above, any missing information, illustrations, and so on can easily be noted and further material inserted as required.

(d) At this stage, too, in some personal studies a certain amount of practical work, such as testing material or constructions, or arranging samples or specimens, may be needed.

### The report – presentation

The way in which the report is presented is important. Neat work, well set out, reflects a tidy, craftsman's type of mind, and will create a favourable impression.

Generally speaking, a loose-leaf folder is often the best way of presenting the written part of a study, as extra pages, drawings and leaflets can be inserted just where they are needed. Sheets of mounted and neatly labelled small specimens can be kept in a separate envelope-type folder, and larger specimens, examples, or test pieces can be laid out on a sheet of hardboard or some other plain surface. If there are numbers of specimens, models, or other 'hardware', provide a neatly-labelled key which can be conveniently positioned on the baseboard with the title of the project.

## A selection of topics for the personal study

NOTE: *bear in mind that the suggestions listed below are just a few of the many topics which can be explored. A number of topics overlap from one general heading to another.*

## Adhesives
(see also pages 53–5)
(a) Do-it-yourself testing for strength, water-resistance, etc.
(b) Glue-making.
(c) Effect of temperature on setting (curing) times.

*Sources of information*
Borden Chemical (UK) Ltd, North Baddesley, Southampton (*Casco*, etc.)
Bostik Ltd, Leicester
CIBA, Duxford, Cambridgeshire (*Aerolite*, *Araldite*, etc.)
Croid Ltd, Berkshire House, 168 High Holborn, London WC1
Evode Ltd, Common Road, Stafford (*Evostik*, etc.)

## Aircraft
– the use of wood in aircraft
(a) Early flying machines and wooden aeroplanes.
(b) The Mosquito (World War II aeroplane).
(c) Gliders.
(d) Kites.

*Books and other sources of information*
M. Cumming   *The Powerless Ones: gliding in peace and war*   Muller, 1966
C. Hart   *Kites: an historical survey*   Faber, 1967
C. Hart   *Your Book of Kites*   Faber, 1970

C. M. Sharp and M. J. F. Bowyer   *Mosquito* Faber, 1967
C. H. Gibbs-Smith   *The Aeroplane*   HMSO, 1960
A. H. Wheeler   *Building Aeroplanes for 'Those Magnificent Men'*   Foulis, 1965
*Flight International* (weekly)
*Look out for:* the collection in the Science Museum, South Kensington, London; the Shuttleworth Trust collection of historic aeroplanes, Biggleswade, Bedfordshire.

## Antiques
(a) A chosen period (e.g. the eighteenth century).
(b) A designer/craftsman (e.g. Chippendale).
(c) A particular article or group of articles (e.g. the development of chairs, or chests).

*Books and other sources of information*
A. E. Bradshaw   *Handmade Woodwork of the Twentieth Century*   Murray, 1962
J. Gloag   *A Social History of Furniture Design* Cassell, 1966
C. H. Hayward   *English Period Furniture*   Evans Bros., 1966
R. Lister   *Great Craftsmen*   Bell, 1962
E. H. Pinto   *The Craftsman in Wood*   Bell, 1962
J. C. Rogers   *English Furniture*   Spring Books, 1968
*Look out for:* the collection in the Victoria and Albert Museum, London (catalogues available); 'stately homes' open to the public; antique shops.

## Boat-building
(see also pages 146–9)
(a) Canoes, dinghies, yachts, and sand yachts.
(b) Specialised methods of boat-building (e.g. laminated plywood, glass-fibre, etc.).
(c) History of boat-building, either general, or of one type of boat or ship (e.g. 'China clippers', warships, coracles).

*Books and other sources of information*
H. P. Spratt   *The Birth of the Steam Boat* Griffin, 1958
M. Verney   *Complete Amateur Boat-building in Wood, Glass-fibre and Metal*   Murray, 1967

## Building

(a) The uses of wood in building – an historical survey.

(b) Wooden houses – half-timbered and pre-fabricated houses.

(c) Roof construction – this could be studied historically or in association with structural uses and testing of timber.

*Books and other sources of information*

A. S. Henderson    *The Family House in England*  Dent, 1964

A. Whittick and J. Schreiner    *The Small House today and tomorrow*    Leonard Hill, 1957

Education Secretary, Timber Research and Development Association, Hughenden Valley, High Wycombe, Buckinghamshire

## Carving

(a) Techniques (see Chapter 5).

(b) Carving in churches and cathedrals.

(c) Carved furniture.

(d) The work of one particular carver (e.g. Grinling Gibbons).

(e) Modern carving and wood sculpture.

(f) Treen – historical survey.

*Books and other sources of information*

A. Durst    *Wood Carving*    Studio Vista, 1959

W. T. James    *Treen: a book of gougework*    Pitman, 1950

P. E. Norman    *Sculpture in Wood*    Tiranti, 1962

E. H. Pinto    *Treen and other Wooden Bygones*  Bell, 1969

## Church woodwork

(a) In a particular church or cathedral.

(b) In churches built during a particular period.

(c) One type of church furniture (e.g. choir stalls, screens, pulpits, etc.).

*Books and other sources of information*

G. H. Cook    *The English Mediaeval Parish Church*  Phoenix House, 1954

Guide books to cathedrals and churches

## Forestry

(a) Methods of afforestation.

(b) Geographical survey of world timber supplies.

(c) Survey of British Forestry Commission.

(d) Timber nurseries.

(e) Felling methods, etc.

*Sources of information*

Forestry Commission, 25 Savile Row, London W1

Timber Research and Development Association, Hughenden Valley, High Wycombe, Buckinghamshire

Princes Risborough Laboratory, The Building Research Station, Princes Risborough, Buckinghamshire

## Furniture (see Chapter 10)

(a) The work of one modern designer.

(b) The effect of the uses of modern materials on furniture design.

(c) Designing an interior, or a group of furniture.

(d) A study of the work of a local cabinet-maker, or a local furniture manufacturer.

*Books and other sources of information*

See list on page 152, and

L. Abbatt    *The Stanley Book of Designs for Making Your Own Furniture*    Spectator, 1966

Dennis and Barbara Young    *Furniture in Britain Today*    Tiranti, 1964

Catalogues from furniture manufacturers

*Look out for*: the Design Centre, Haymarket, London SW1; local shops and factories.

## Manufacture of wooden boards

(a) Survey of plywood, blockboard, chipboard, etc.

(b) Comparison tests.

(c) Investigation into different methods of jointing.

*Sources of information*

British Plimber Ltd, Dovers Corner, New Road, Rainham, Essex

The Airscrew Co and Jicwood Ltd (Weyroc), Weybridge, Surrey

Timber Research and Development Association, Hughenden Valley, High Wycombe, Buckinghamshire

Princes Risborough Laboratory, The Building Research Station, Princes Risborough, Buckinghamshire

## Methods of construction
Laminating:
(a) Mass production methods.
(b) Hand methods for special purposes.
(c) Survey of use of laminating techniques.
(d) Timber arch construction.
(e) Comparison between strength of laminated, solid and jointed wooden structures, models, beams, arches, bridges, etc.

Bending: bentwood furniture, etc.

*Books and other sources of information*
*The Steam Bending Properties of Various Timbers* HMSO, 1967
Flexitools Ltd, Albrighton, Wolverhampton, Staffordshire

## Musical instruments
(a) The history of (i) woodwind, (ii) percussion, (iii) strings.
(b) Manufacture of any of these (e.g. recorders, xylophone, violin).
(c) Investigation into vibrations and resonance of differently-shaped sound boxes, using different timbers and thicknesses of wood.

*Books and other sources of information*
R. Roberts *Musical Instruments Made to be Played* Dryad Press, 1965

## Rural crafts
(see pages 149–151)
(a) Local crafts and craftsmen (e.g. basket-making).
(b) Survey of rural craftwork in use in the locality (e.g. on the farm).
(c) Investigation into methods of making one type of equipment (e.g. wattle fencing).

## Sports equipment (see pages 158–160)
History of the manufacture of:
(a) Cricket bats.
(b) Hockey sticks.
(c) Tennis racquets.
(d) Archery equipment.

## Timber – milling and marketing
Importing, timber yard management, conversion, machinery, measurement, standard terms, grading and selling.

## Timber – trees
(a) Growth.
(b) Biological survey of local trees.
(c) Comparison of structure (grain), bark, growing conditions, faults, etc., in different timbers.
(d) Timber pests – insect and fungoid attack of trees and worked timber.
(e) Timber properties – strength testing, resistance to decay, hardness and wear resistance, etc.

*Books and other sources of information*
H. E. Desch *Timber* Macmillan, 1968 (Rather advanced)
B. A. Jay *Timber* Ward Lock Educational, 1964
Pamphlets, such as:
*Handbook of Hardwoods* Ministry of Technology Laboratory, HMSO, 1970
*Handbook of Softwoods* Ministry of Technology Laboratory, HMSO, 1968
Timber Research and Development Association booklets

## Timber – finishes
(a) Survey and testing of paints, lacquers, etc.
(b) Preservatives and their efficiency.
(c) Paint manufacture and application.

*Books and other sources of information*
C. H. Hayward *Staining and Polishing (Woodworker Handbooks)* Evans Bros, 1962
R. Scharff *Complete Book of Wood Finishing* Faber, 1968
Leaflets from any paint or polish manufacturer

## Tools

(a) Evolution of tools (e.g. planes, saws).
(b) General history of woodworking tools.
(c) Tool manufacture.
(d) Special tools for certain trades (e.g. clogmaking).

*Books and other sources of information*
P. Child    *The Craftsman Woodturner*   Bell, 1971
H. T. Evans    *The Craft of Woodturning*   Technical Press, 1968
W. L. Goodman    *History of Woodworking Tools* Bell, 1964
G. T. James    *Woodturning : design and practice* Murray, 1958
F. Pain    *The Practical Woodturner*   Evans Bros, 1961
P. Wright    *Old Farm Implements*   Black, 1961

## Wooden weapons

(a) Survey of ancient wooden weapons and war equipment (e.g. catapults).
(b) Making and testing models of these pieces of equipment.

*Books and other sources of information*
R. Payne-Gallwey    *The Crossbow*   Wheaton, 1958

# Index